EASY PIANO

Imagine

C000018957

Order No. HLE90000242

ISBN 0-7119-6451-3

*Unauthorised reproduction of any part of this publication by any means
including photocopying is an infringement of copyright.*

Exclusive distributors:

Music Sales Limited

8/9 Frith Street, London W1V 5TZ, England

Music Sales Pty Limited

120 Rothschild Avenue, Rosebery, NSW 2018, Australia

Cover design by Pearce Marchbank, Studio Twenty, London.

Cover photographs courtesy of Pictor International.

Printed in the U.S.A.

Your Guarantee of Quality

As publishers, we strive to produce every book
to the highest commercial standards.
This book has been carefully designed to minimise awkward
page turns and to make playing from it a real pleasure.
Throughout, the printing and binding have been planned
to ensure a sturdy, attractive publication which
should give years of enjoyment.
If your copy fails to meet our high standards,
please inform us and we will gladly replace it.

*Music Sales' complete catalogue describes thousands of titles and is
available in full colour sections by subject, direct from Music Sales Limited.
Please state your areas of interest and send a cheque/postal order for £1.50 for postage to:
Music Sales Limited, Newmarket Road, Bury St. Edmunds, Suffolk IP33 3YB, England.*

Visit the Internet Music Shop at
http://www.musicsales.co.uk

Contents

Hal Leonard Europe
Distributed by Music Sales

*This publication is not authorised for sale in
the United States of America and/or Canada.*

ALL YOU NEED IS LOVE

Words and Music by JOHN LENNON
and PAUL McCARTNEY

There's noth-ing you can do that can't be done.
Noth-ing you can make that can't be made.
Noth-ing you can know that is - n't known.

Noth-ing you can sing that can't be sung.
No one you can save that can't be saved.
Noth-ing you can see that is - n't shown.

Noth-ing you can say but you can learn how to play the game,
Noth-ing you can do but you can learn how to be you in time,
No-where you can be that is - n't where you're meant to be,

It's

eas - y:

4

BLOWIN' IN THE WIND

Words and Music by
BOB DYLAN

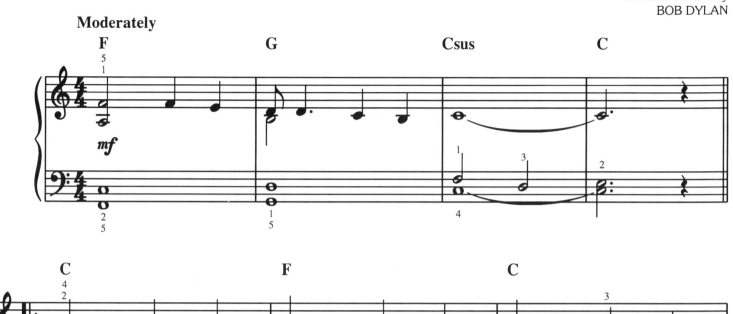

How man - y roads must a man walk _____
How man - y times must a man look _____
How man - y years can a moun - tain ex -

down be - fore you call him a
up be - fore he can see him the _____
ist be - fore it's washed to the

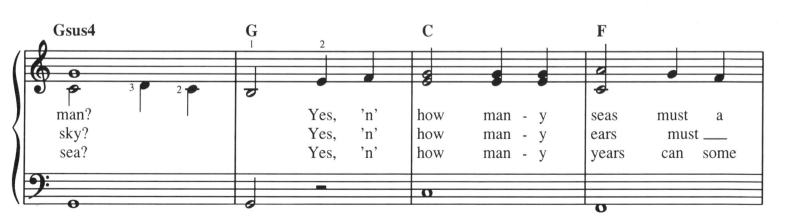

man? Yes, 'n' how man - y seas must a
sky? Yes, 'n' how man - y ears must _____
sea? Yes, 'n' how man - y years can some

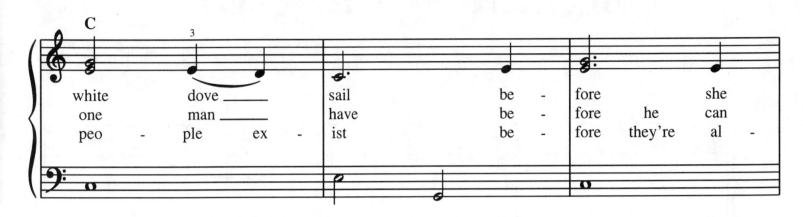

white dove _____ sail be - fore she
one man _____ have be - fore he can
peo - ple ex - ist be - fore they're al -

sleeps in the sand? _____ Yes, 'n' how man - y
hear peo - ple cry? _____ Yes, 'n' how man - y
lowed to be free? _____ Yes, 'n' how man - y

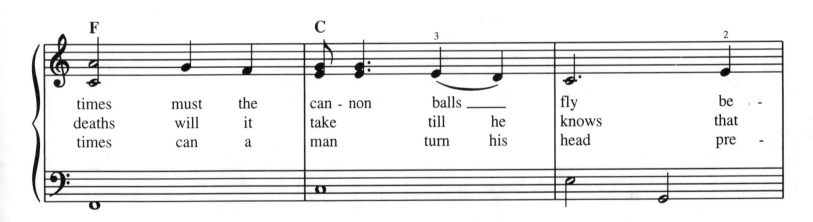

times must the can - non balls _____ fly be -
deaths will it take till he knows that
times can a man turn his head pre -

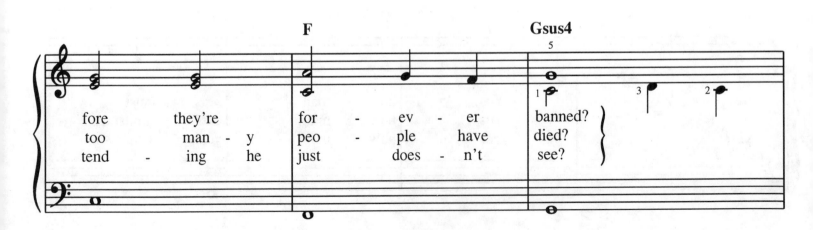

fore they're for - ev - er banned?
too man - y peo - ple have died?
tend - ing he just does - n't see?

BLACKBIRD

Words and Music by JOHN LENNON
and PAUL McCARTNEY

BRIDGE OVER TROUBLED WATER

Words and Music by
PAUL SIMON

Moderately, not too bright

When you're / (When you're) wea - ry,___ down and out,___ feel - in'___ When you're on the

___ small, / street, When tears are in / When eve - ning falls in your eyes,___ / so hard,___

I'll dry them all. / I will com - fort___ you.

I'm on your side.___ / I'll take your part.___ Oh,___ when times___ get / Oh,___ when dark - ness

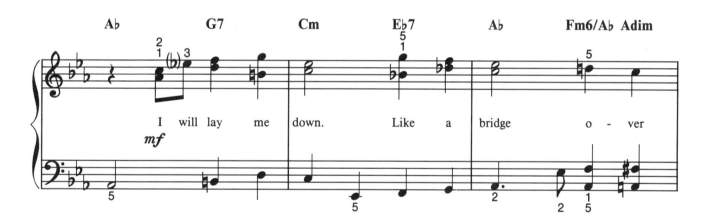

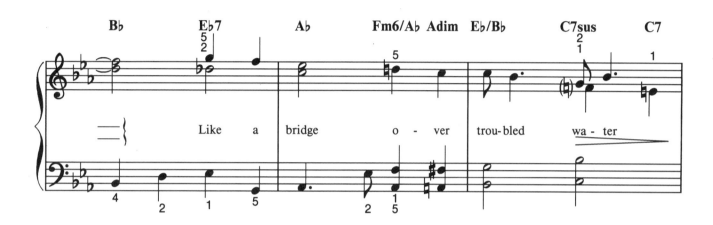

11

12

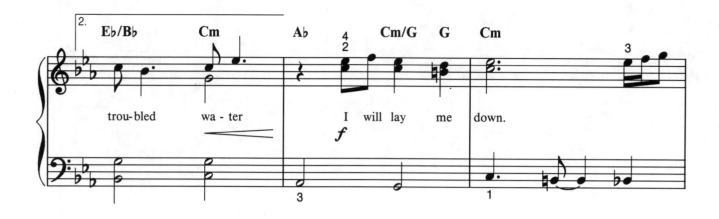

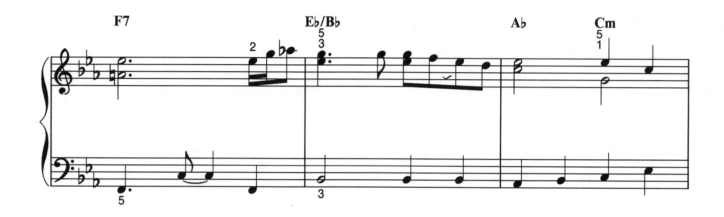

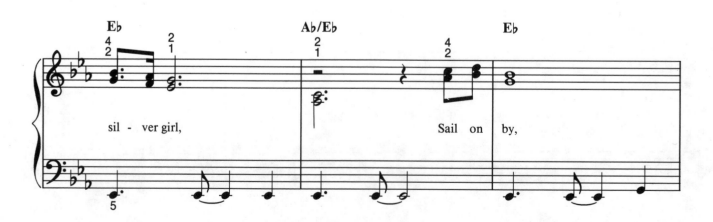

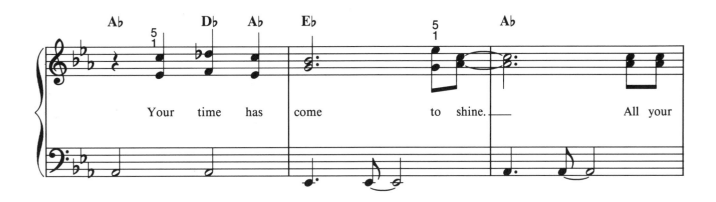

Your time has come to shine. All your

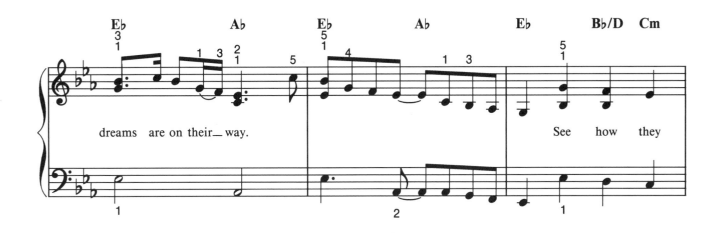

dreams are on their way. See how they

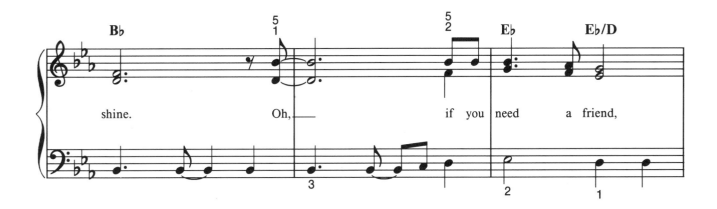

shine. Oh, if you need a friend,

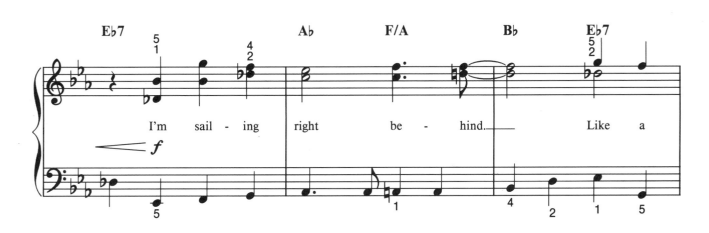

I'm sail - ing right be - hind. Like a

14

CANDLE ON THE WATER

from Walt Disney's PETE'S DRAGON

Words and Music by AL KASHA
and JOEL HIRSCHHORN

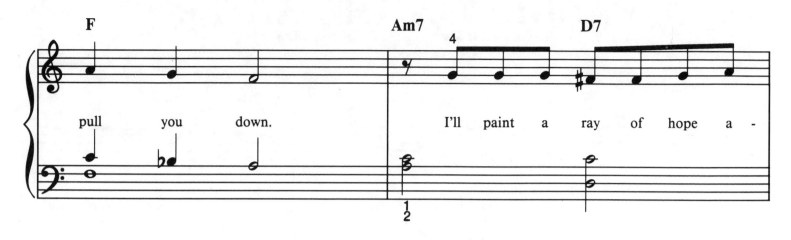

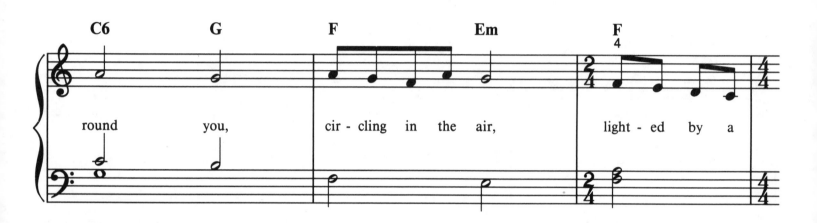

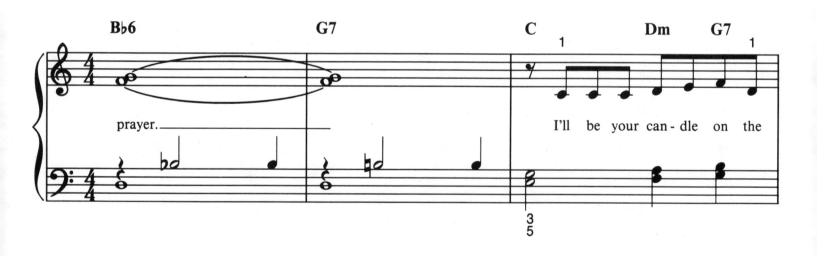

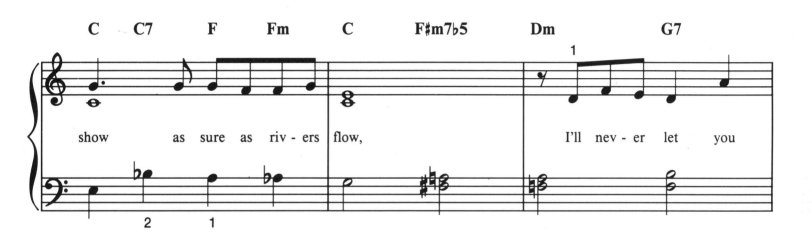

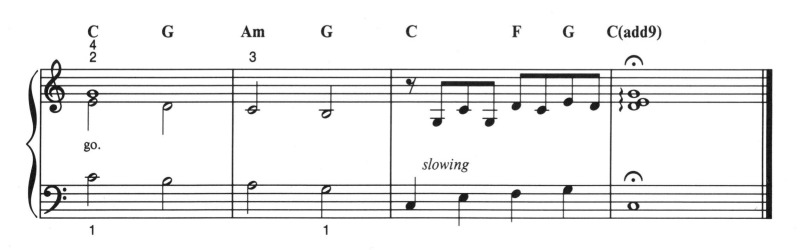

CIRCLE OF LIFE

Music by ELTON JOHN
Lyrics by TIM RICE

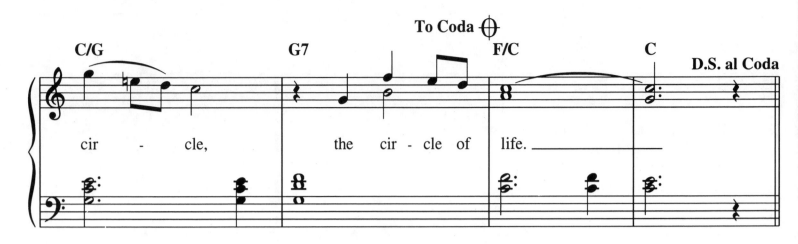

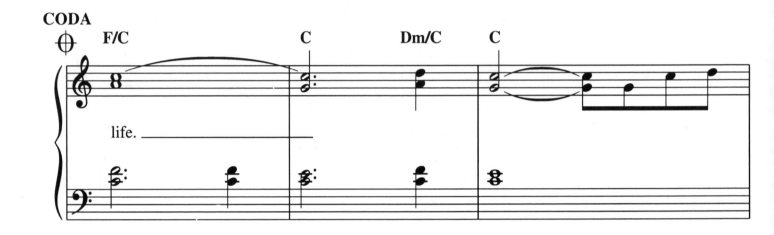

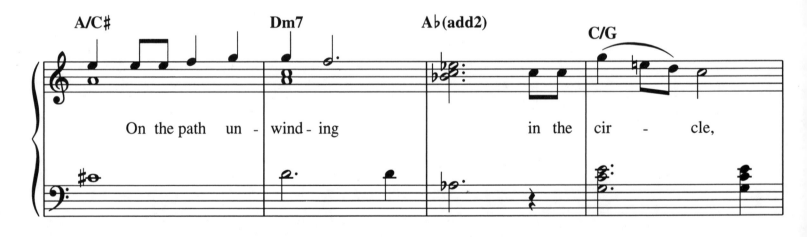

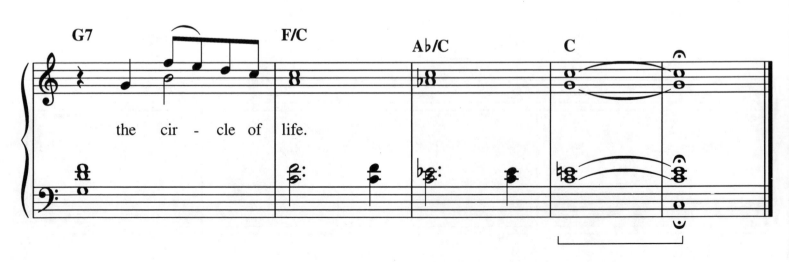

COLORS OF THE WIND
from Walt Disney's POCAHONTAS

Music by ALAN MENKEN
Lyrics by STEPHEN SCHWARTZ

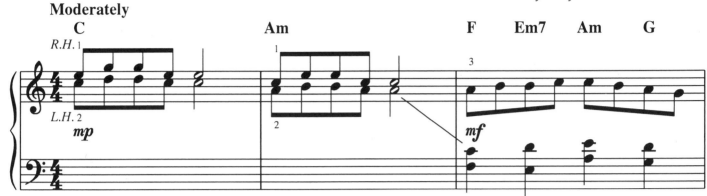

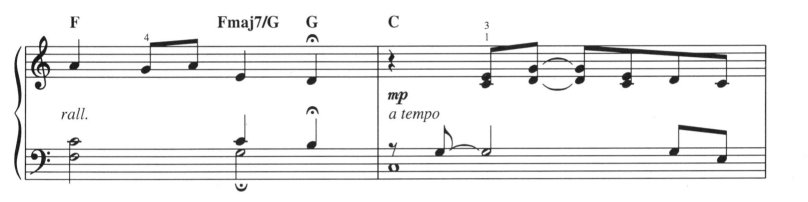

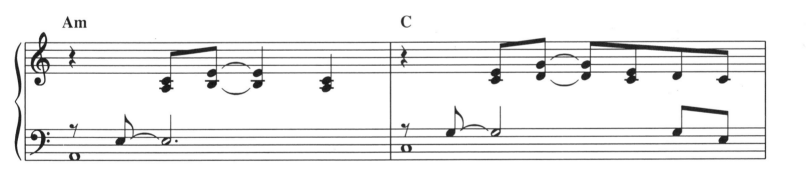

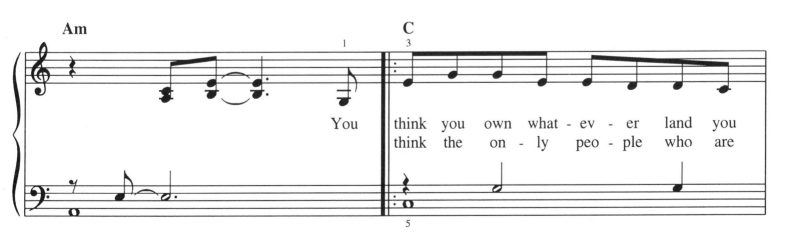

You think you own what-ev-er land you
think the on-ly peo-ple who are

land on; _____ the
peo - ple are the

earth is just a dead thing you can
peo - ple who look and think like

claim; but
you, but

I know ev - 'ry rock and tree and
if you walk the foot - steps of a

crea - ture has a
strang - er you'll learn

1.

life, has a spir - it, has a

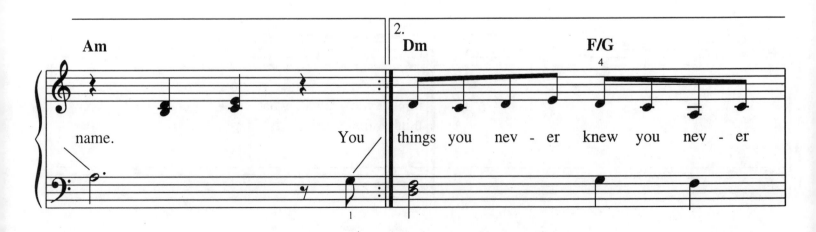

name.

2.

You things you nev - er knew you nev - er

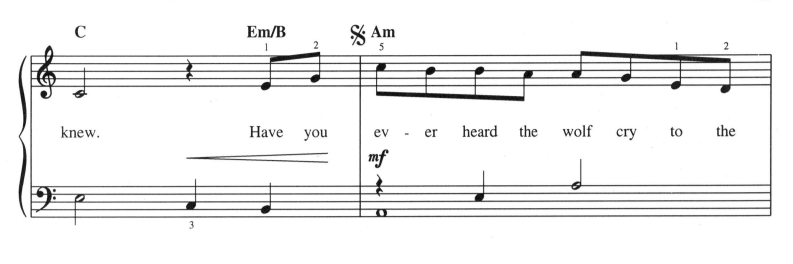

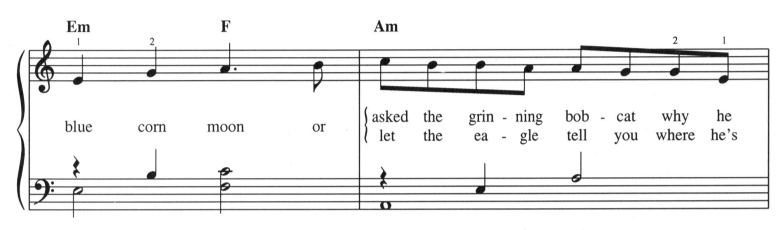

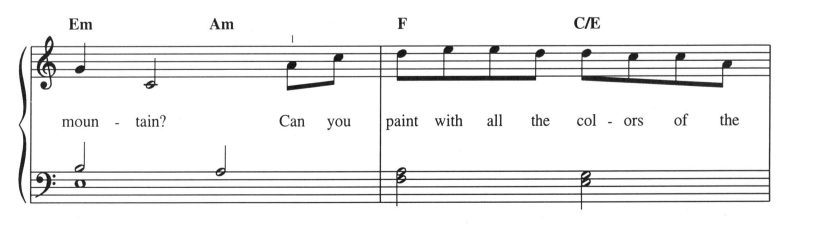

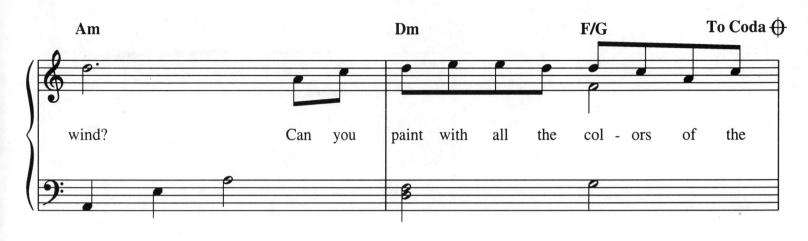

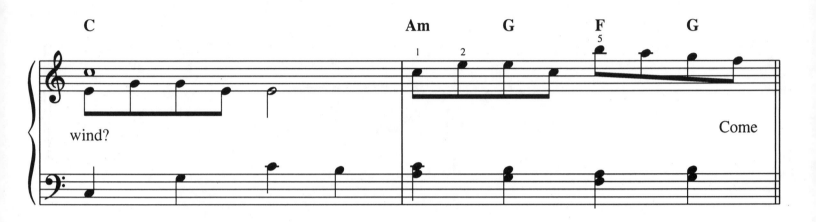

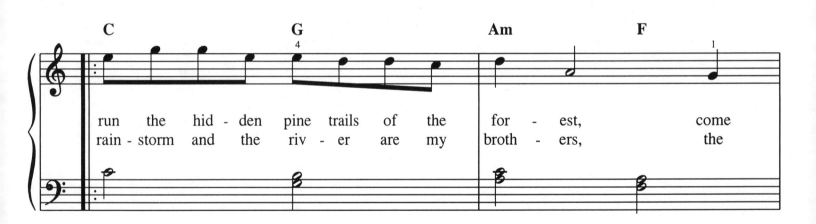

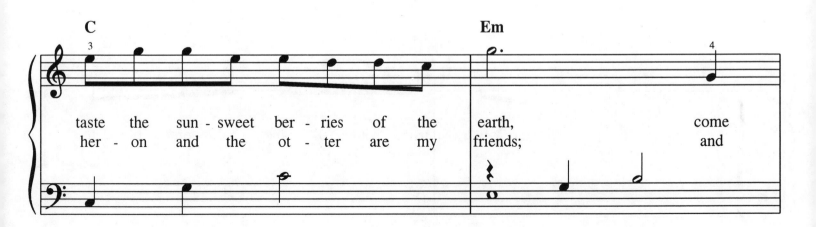

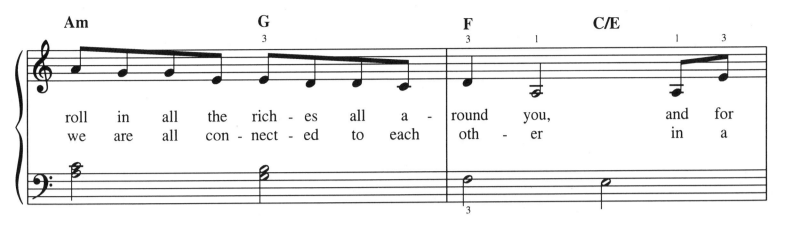

roll in all the rich - es all a - round you, and for
we are all con - nect - ed to each oth - er in a

1.
once nev - er won - der what they're worth. The

2. D.S. al Coda

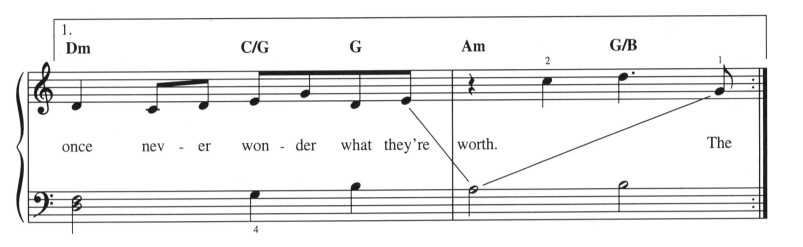

cir - cle, in a hoop that nev - er ____ ends. ___ Have you

CODA

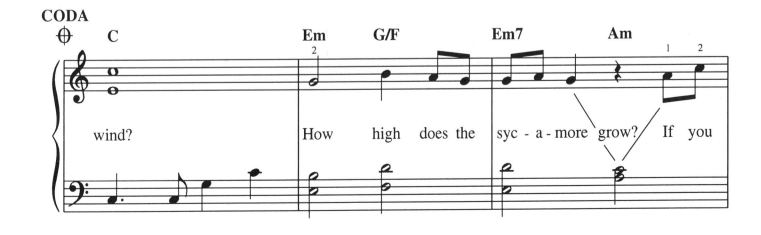

wind? How high does the syc - a - more grow? If you

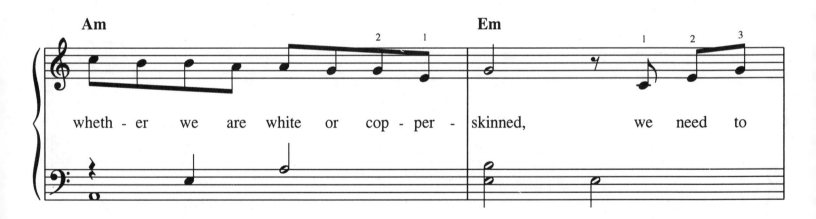

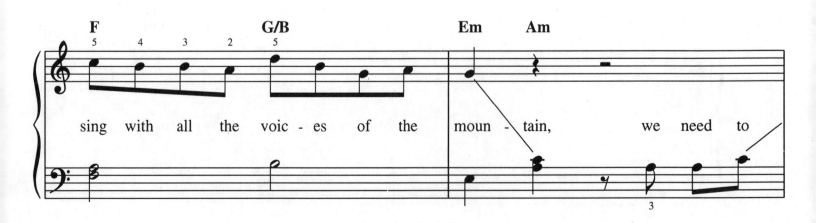

EBONY AND IVORY

Words and Music by
McCARTNEY

29

THE 59TH STREET BRIDGE SONG
(Feelin' Groovy)

Words and Music by
PAUL SIMON

Moderately

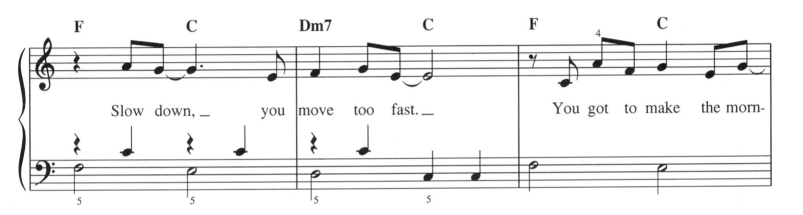

Slow down, _ you move too fast. _ You got to make the morn-

- ing last. Just kick-in' down the cob - ble stones, _

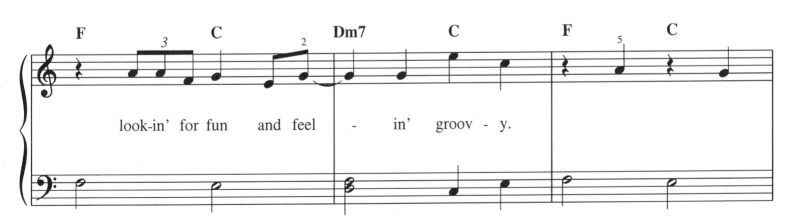

look-in' for fun and feel - in' groov - y.

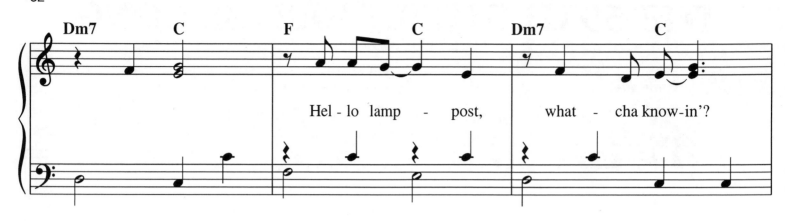

Hel - lo lamp - post, what - cha know-in'?

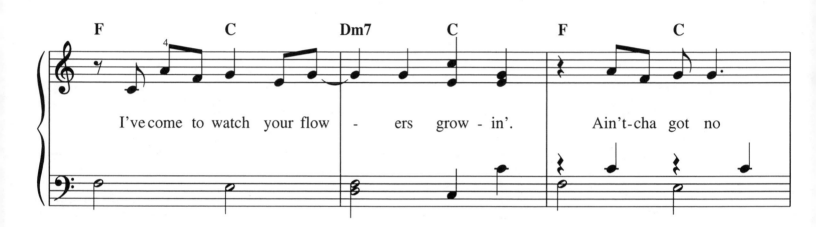

I've come to watch your flow - ers grow - in'. Ain't-cha got no

rhymes for me? Doot - in' doo - doo, feel - in' groov - y.

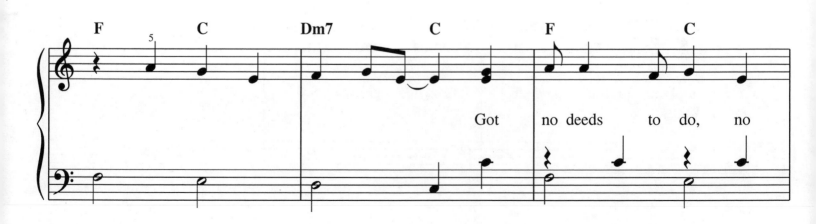

Got no deeds to do, no

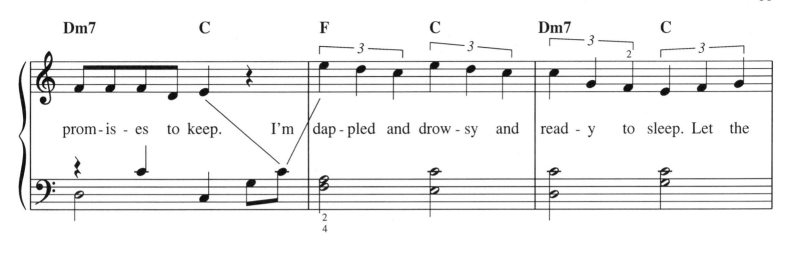

prom-is-es to keep. I'm dap-pled and drow-sy and read-y to sleep. Let the

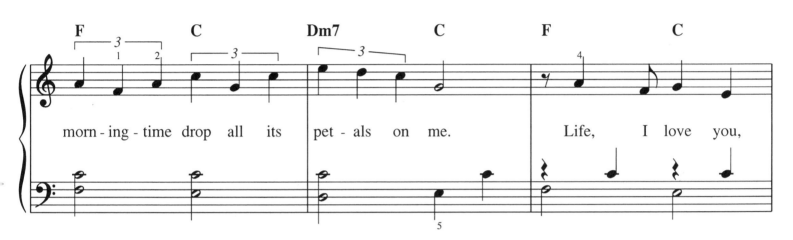

morn-ing-time drop all its pet-als on me. Life, I love you,

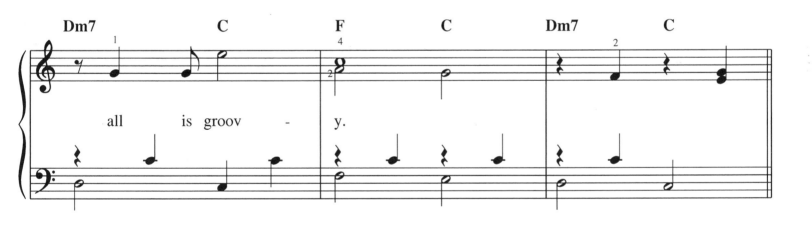

all is groov - y.

Repeat and Fade

THE FLOWER THAT SHATTERED THE STONE

Words and Music by JOHN JARVIS
and JOE HENRY

earth   is   our   moth- er,   just   turn- ing   a -
Spar - rows   find   free- dom   be -   hold- ing   the ____

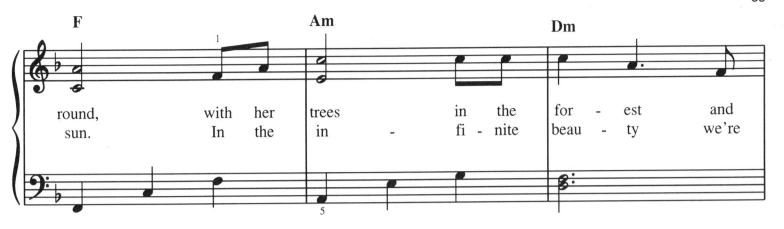

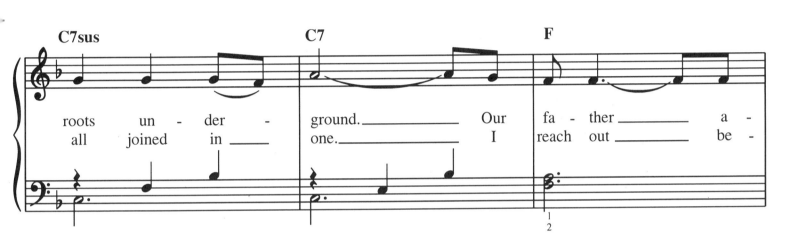

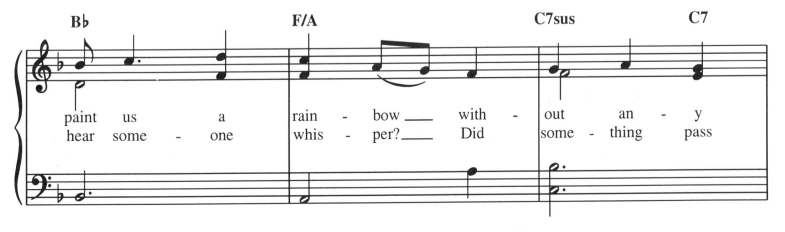

end. _____
by? _____   As the riv - er runs free - ly,   the

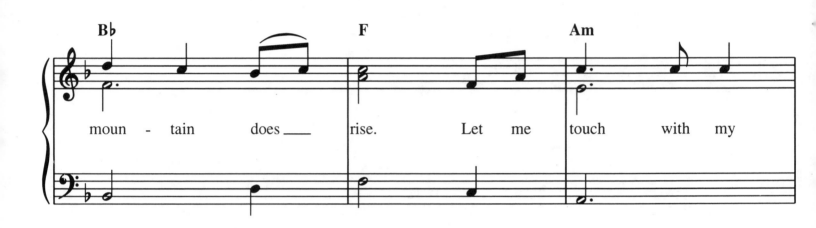

moun - tain does ___ rise.   Let me touch with my

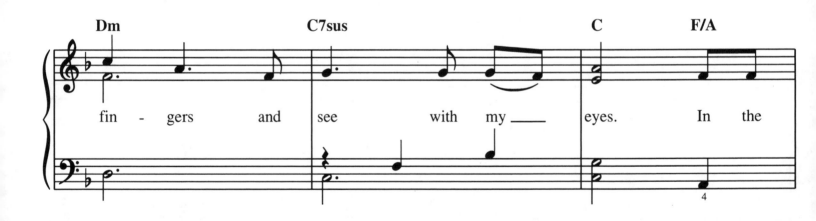

fin - gers and   see with my ___ eyes.   In the

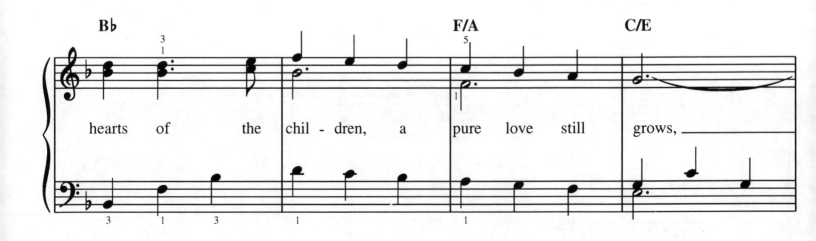

hearts of the chil - dren, a   pure love still   grows, _____

GET TOGETHER

Words and Music by
CHESTER POWERS

moun - tains ring, or make the an - gels
left us here re - turns for us _____ at
key to love and fear all in your trem - bling

cry. _____
last. _____
hand. _____

Know the dove is on the wing, ___ and
We are but a mo - ment's sun - light
One key ___ un - locks them both you know and

you need not ___ know why. _____
fad - ing on the grass. _____
it's at your ___ com - mand. _____

FROM A DISTANCE

Words and Music by
JULIE GOLD

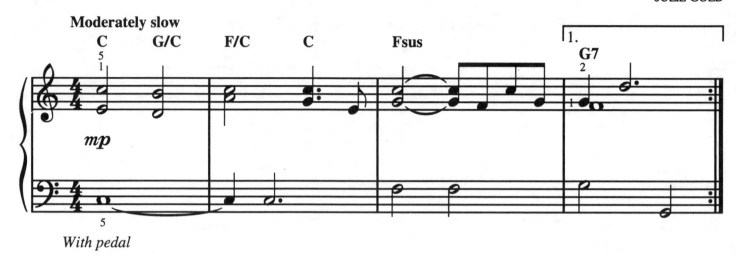

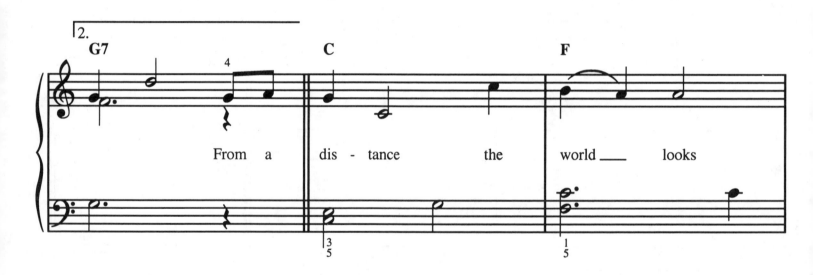

From a dis - tance the world ___ looks

blue and ___ green, _____ and the snow - capped

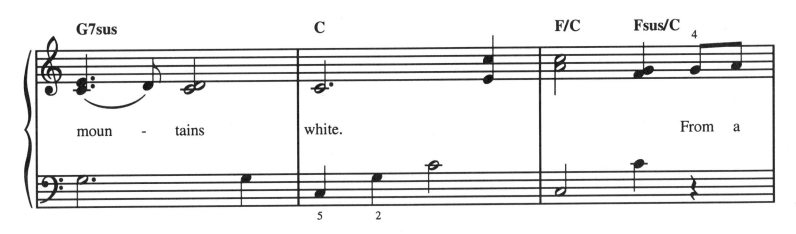

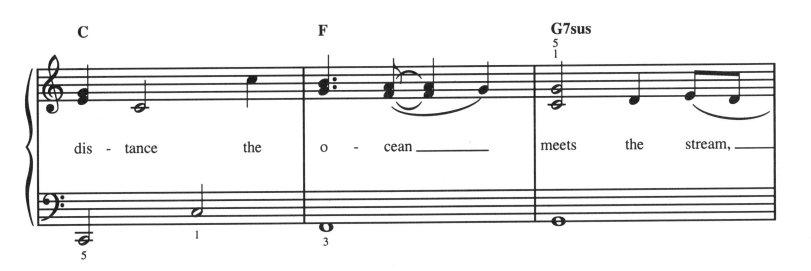

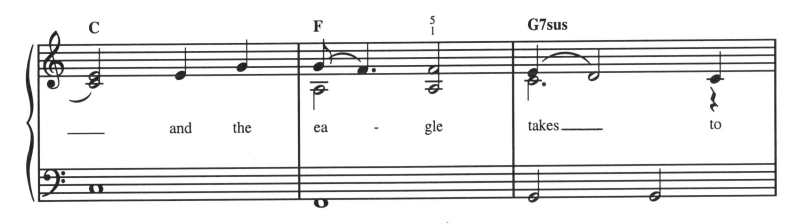

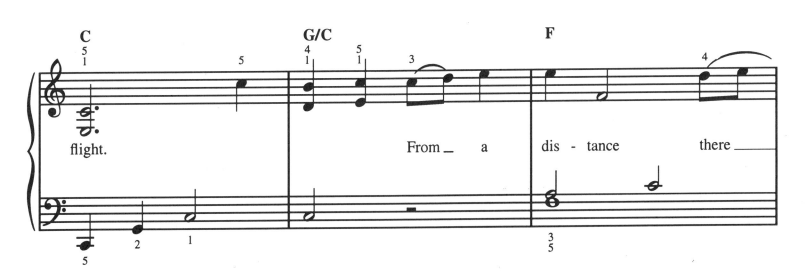

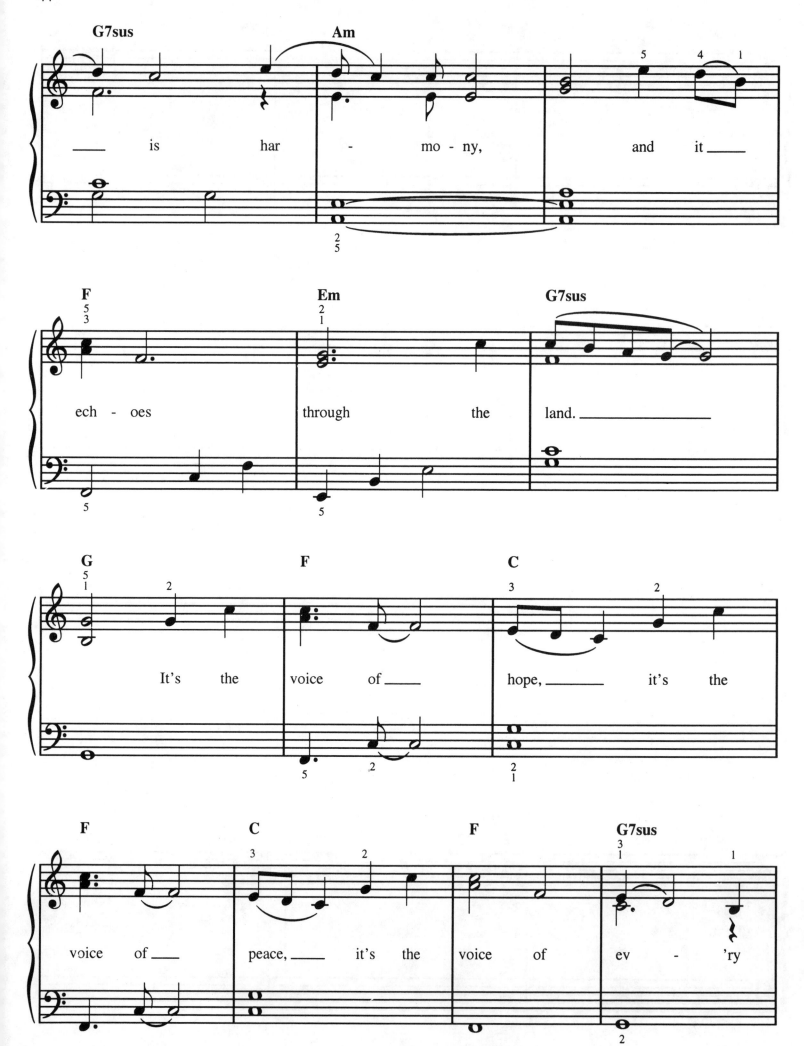

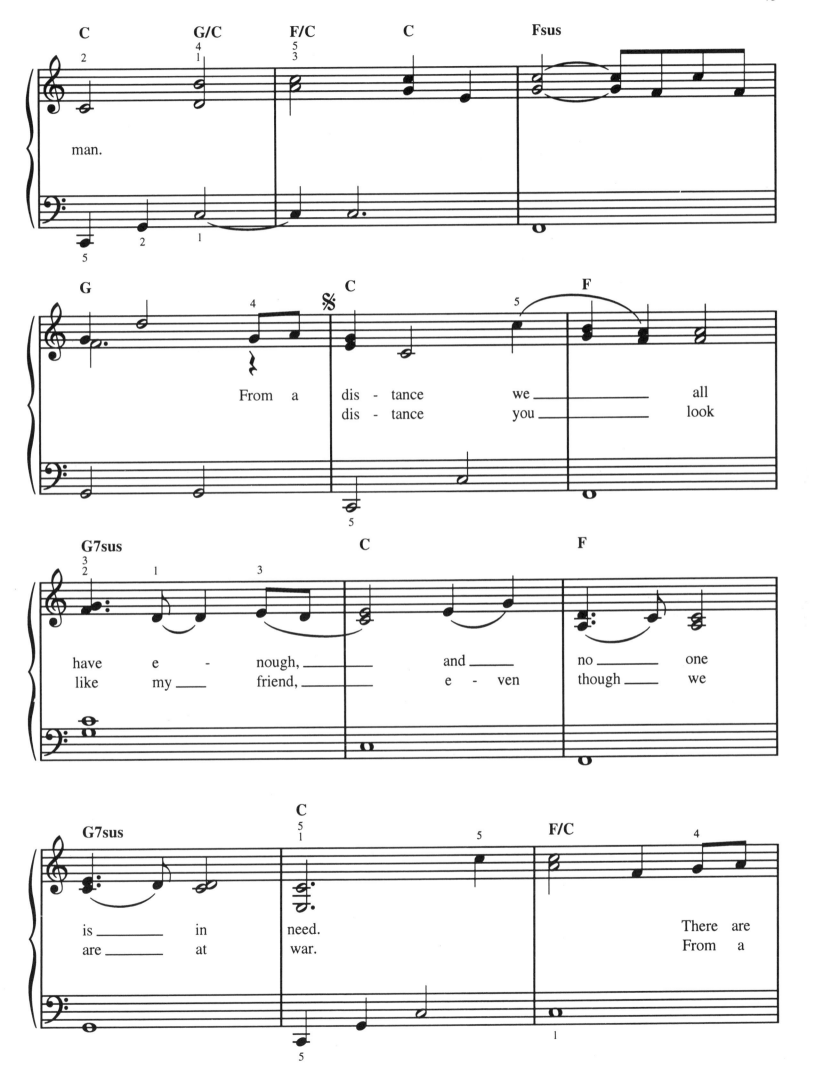

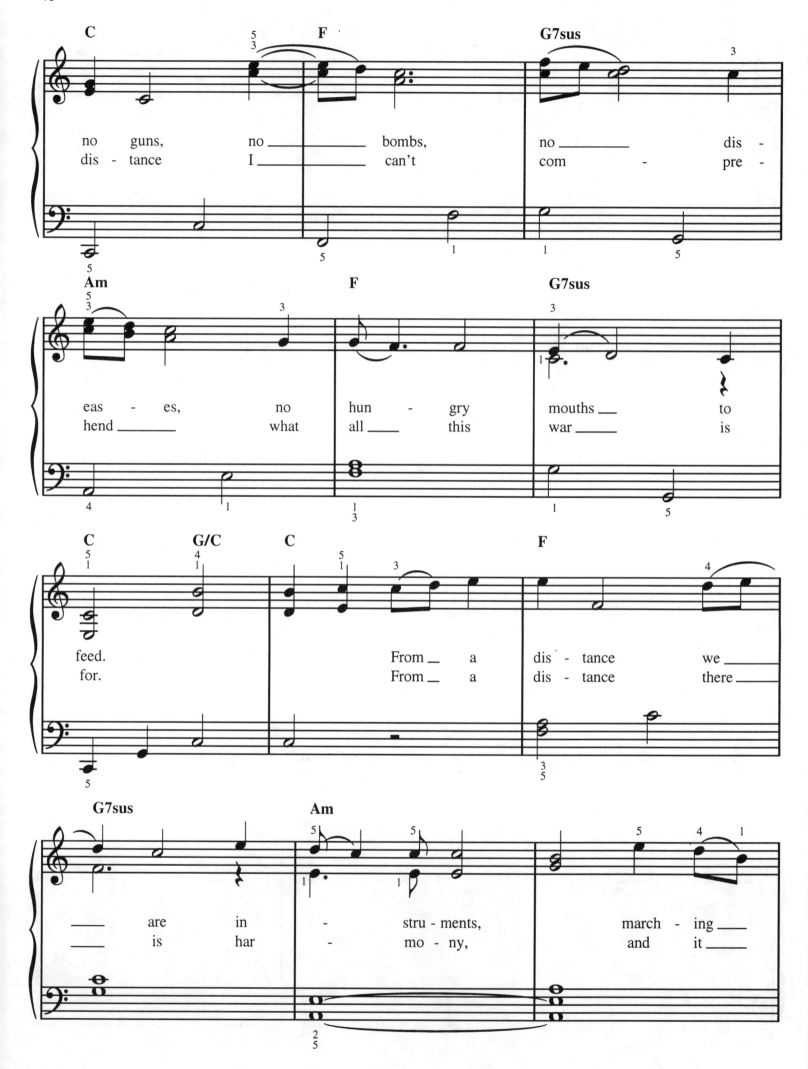

watch - ing us, _____ God _____ is watch - ing us, _____

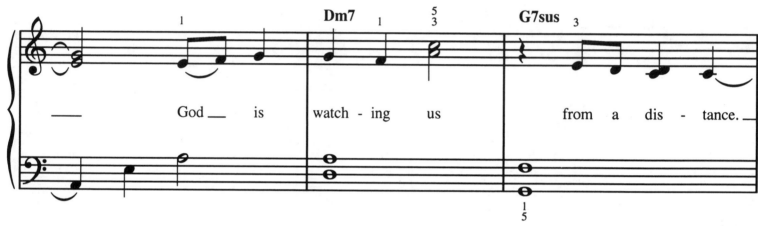

_____ God _____ is watch - ing us from a dis - tance.

_____ From a

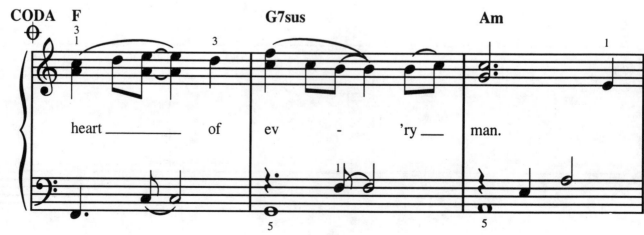

heart _____ of ev - 'ry _____ man.

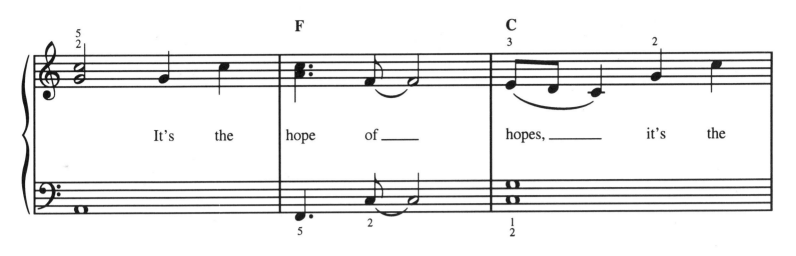

It's the hope of ___ hopes, ___ it's the

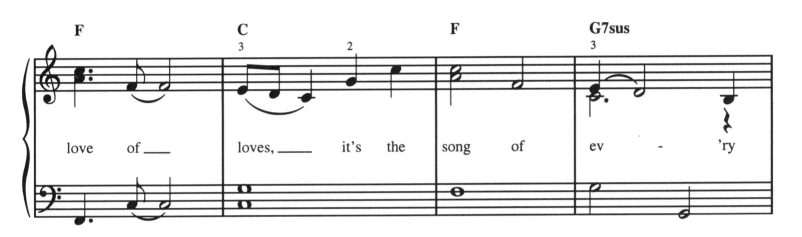

love of ___ loves, ___ it's the song of ev - 'ry

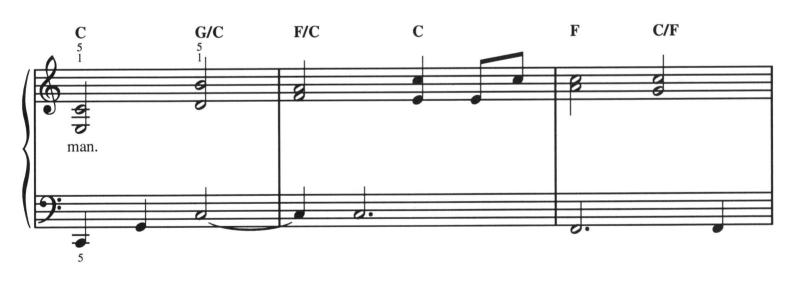

man.

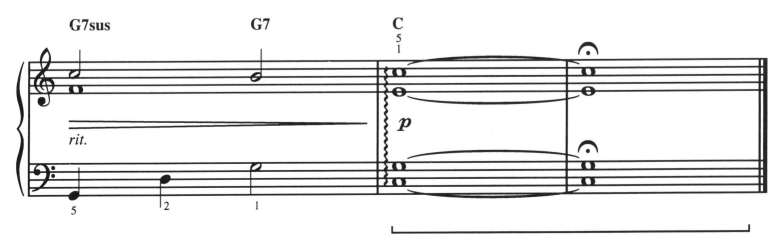

GOD HELP THE OUTCASTS
from Walt Disney's THE HUNCHBACK OF NOTRE DAME

Music by ALAN MENKEN
Lyrics by STEPHEN SCHWARTZ

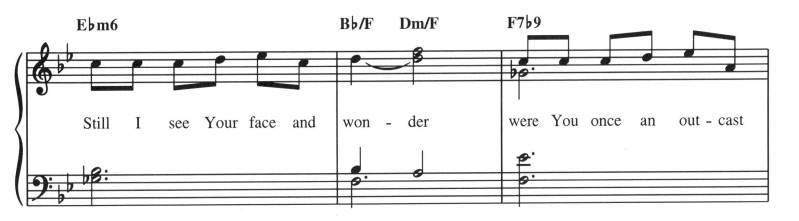

Still I see Your face and won - der were You once an out - cast too?

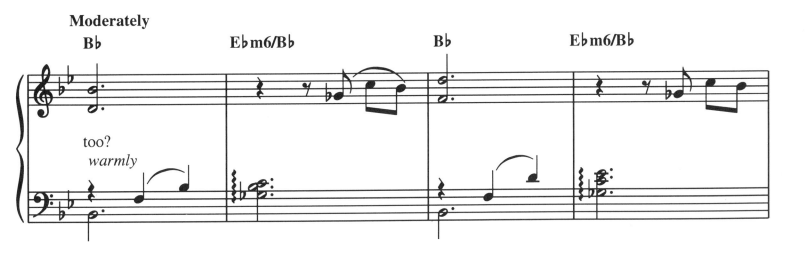

Moderately

warmly

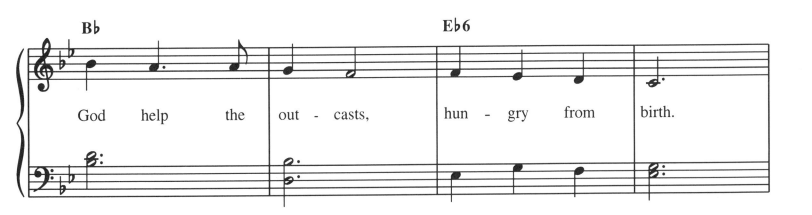

God help the out - casts, hun - gry from birth.

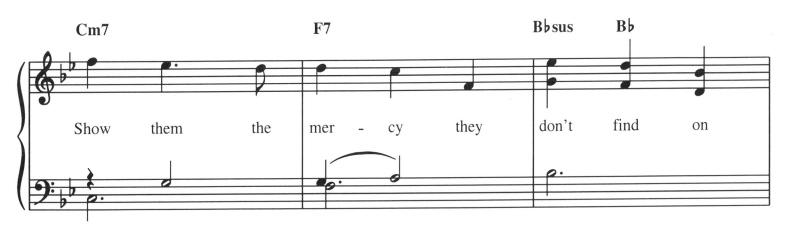

Show them the mer - cy they don't find on

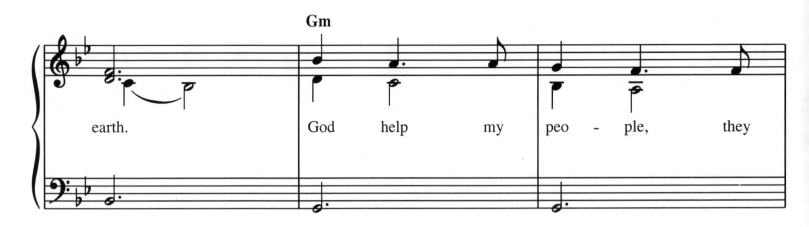

earth. God help my peo - ple, they

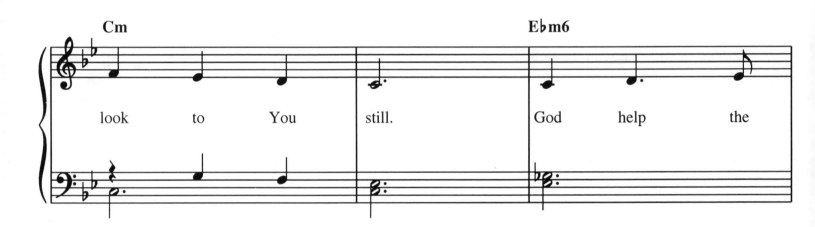

look to You still. God help the

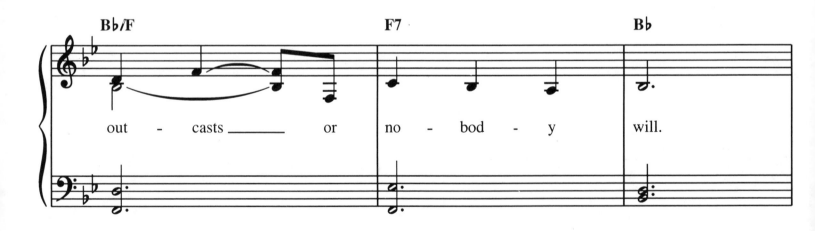

out - casts _____ or no - bod - y will.

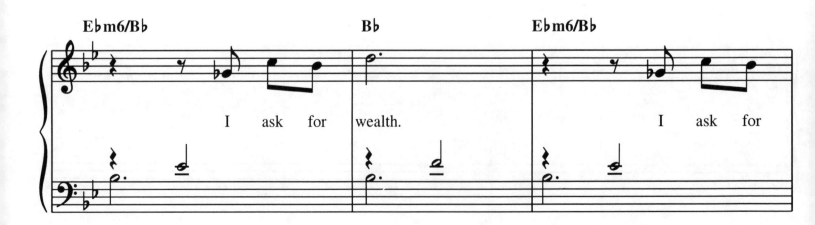

I ask for wealth. I ask for

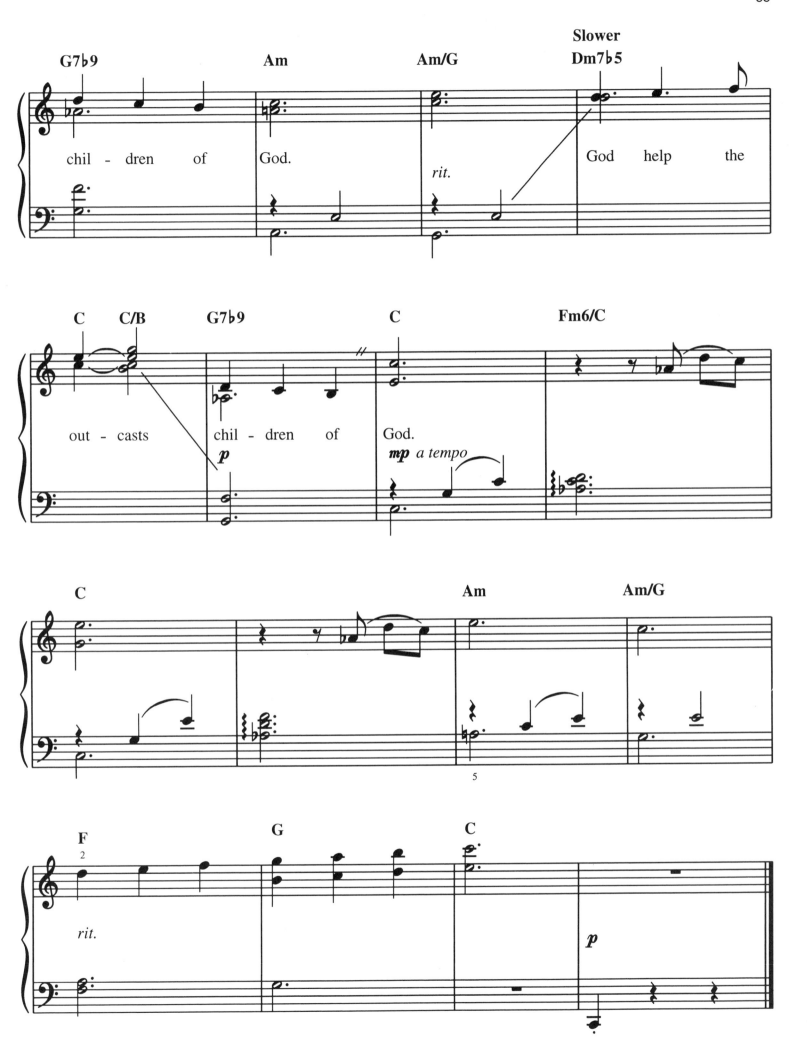

GONNA BUILD A MOUNTAIN
from the Musical Production STOP THE WORLD - I WANT TO GET OFF

Words and Music by LESLIE BRICUSSE
and ANTHONY NEWLEY

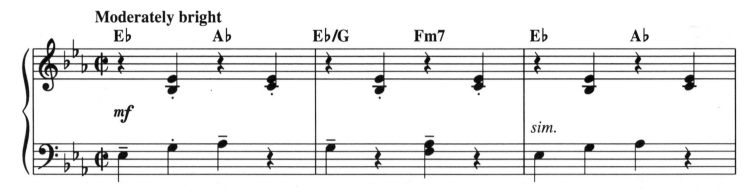

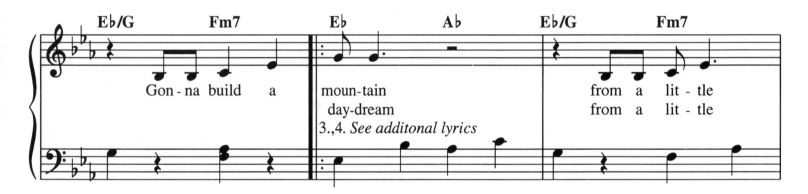

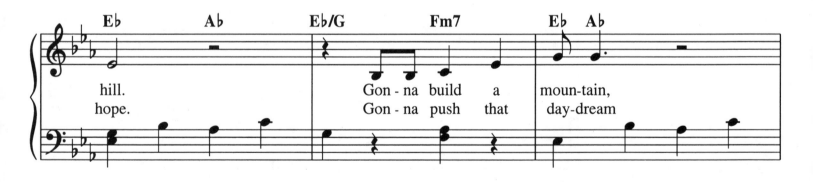

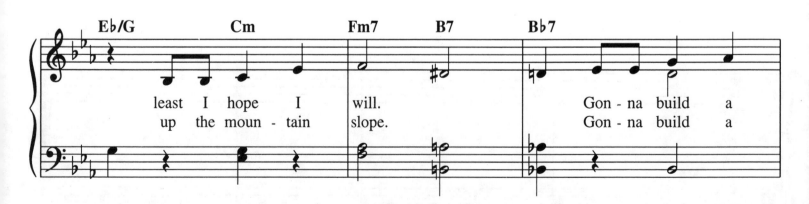

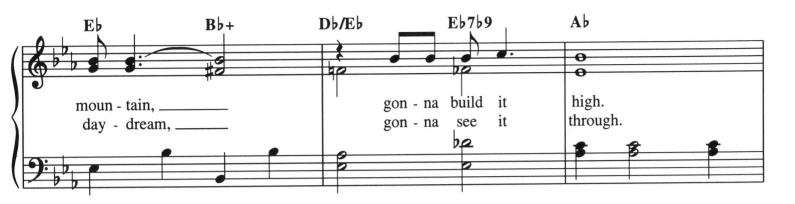

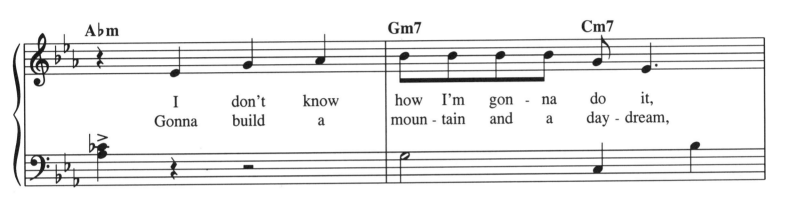

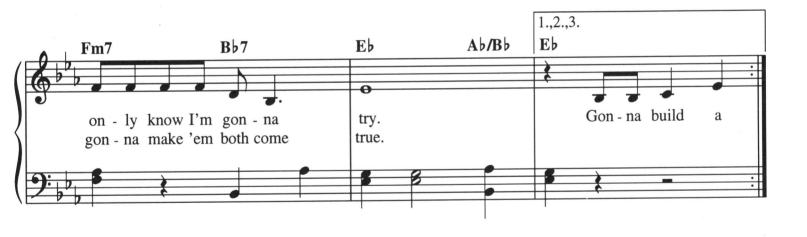

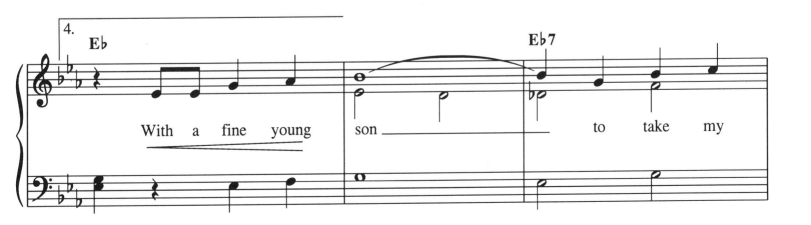

place,   I'll leave a son in my heav - en on

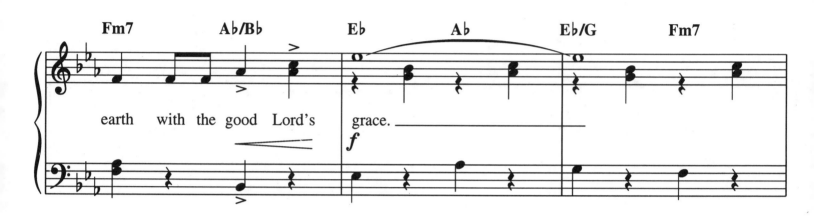

earth with the good Lord's grace. _____

f

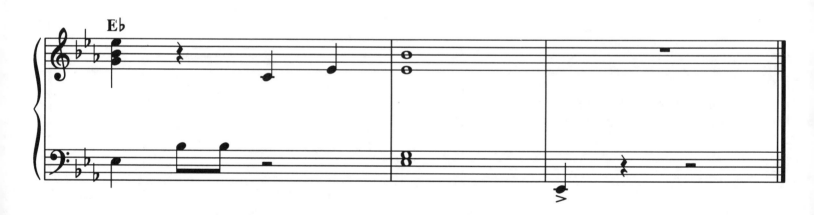

Additional Lyrics

3. Gonna build a heaven from a little hell.
   Gonna build a heaven and I know darn well.
   If I build my mountain with a lot of care.
   And take my daydream up the mountain heaven
      will be waiting there.

4. When I've built that heaven as I will some day
   And the Lord sends Gabriel to take me away,
   Wanna fine young son to take my place
   I'll leave a son in my heaven on earth,
   With the Lord's good grace.

HE AIN'T HEAVY...HE'S MY BROTHER

Words and Music by BOB RUSSELL
and BOBBY SCOTT

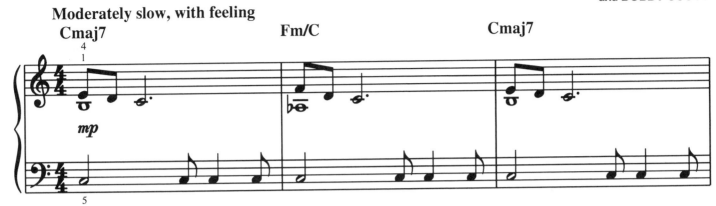

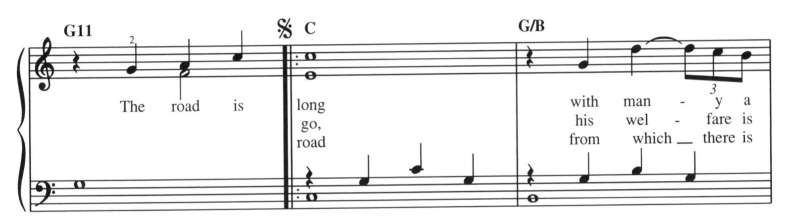

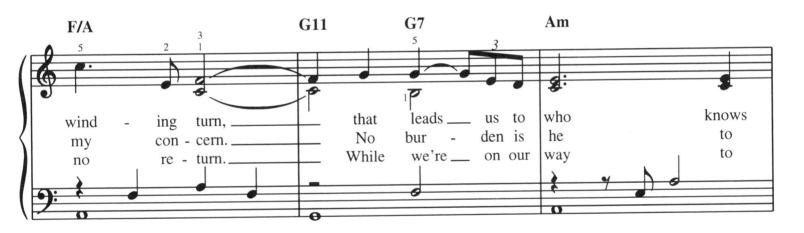

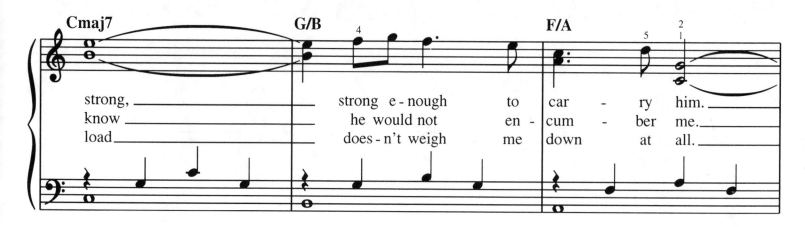

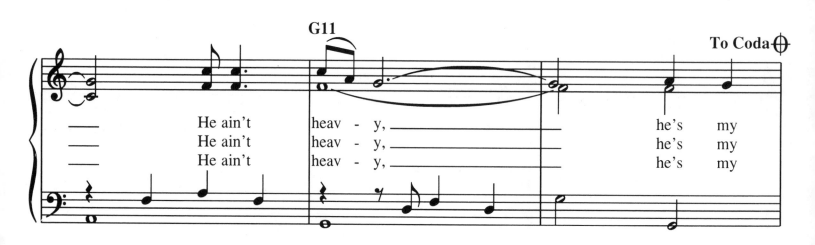

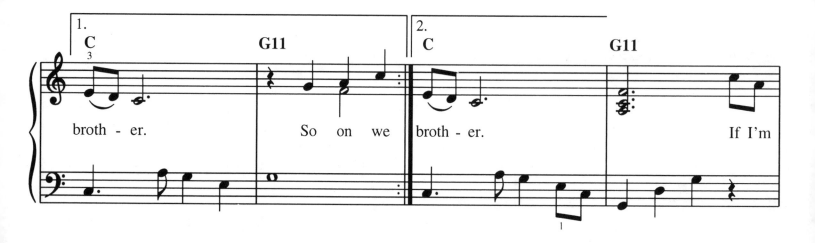

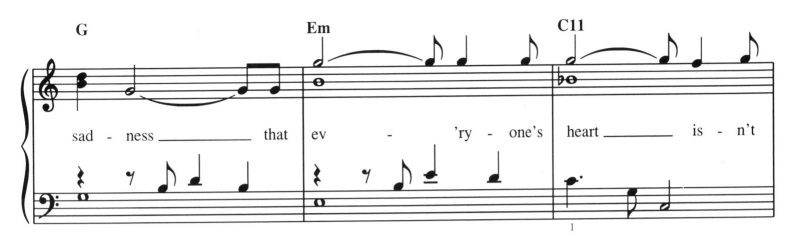

sad - ness _____ that ev - 'ry - one's heart _____ is - n't

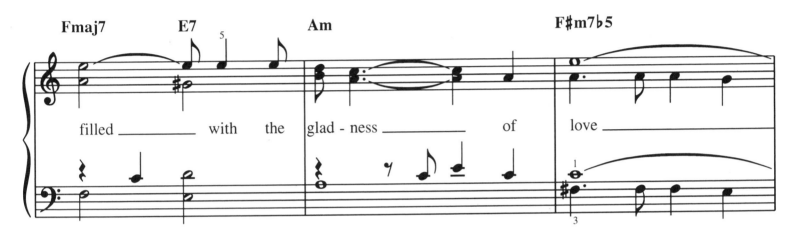

filled _____ with the glad - ness _____ of love _____

_____ for one an - oth - er. _____ It's a long, _ long

broth - er.

I BELIEVE

Words and Music by ERVIN DRAKE, IRVIN GRAHAM,
JIMMY SHIRL and AL STILLMAN

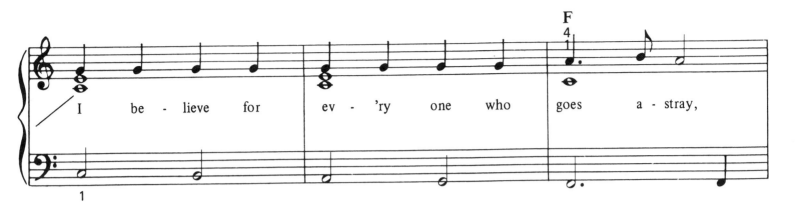

I be - lieve for ev - 'ry one who goes a - stray,

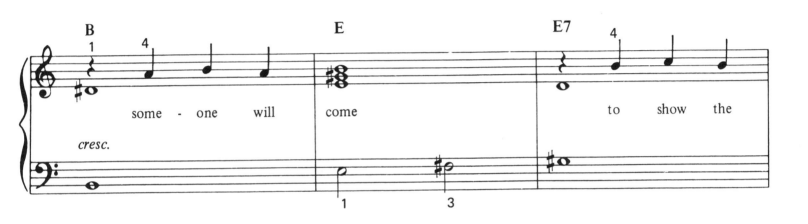

some - one will come to show the

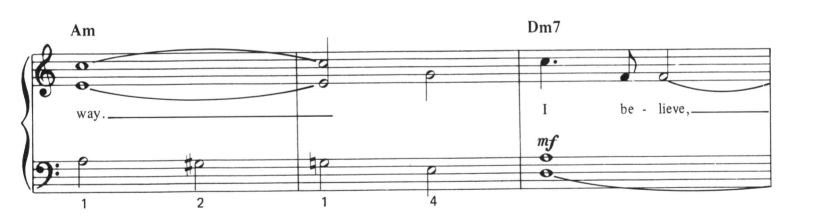

way. I be - lieve,

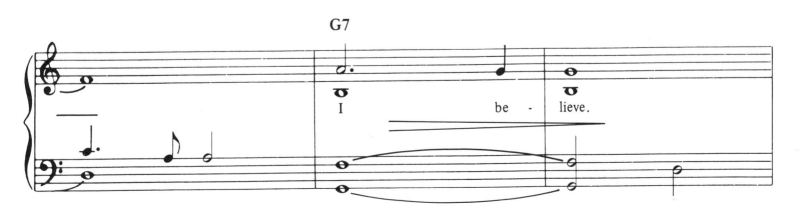

I be - lieve.

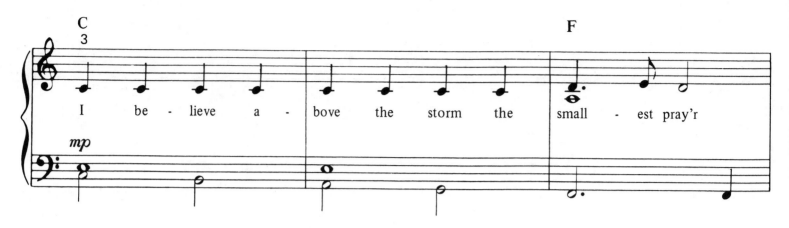

I be - lieve a - bove the storm the small - est pray'r

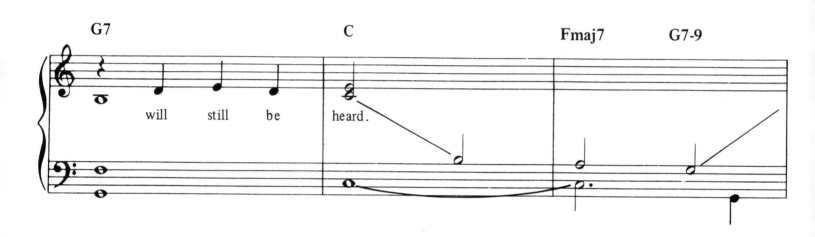

will still be heard.

I be - lieve that some - one in the great some - where

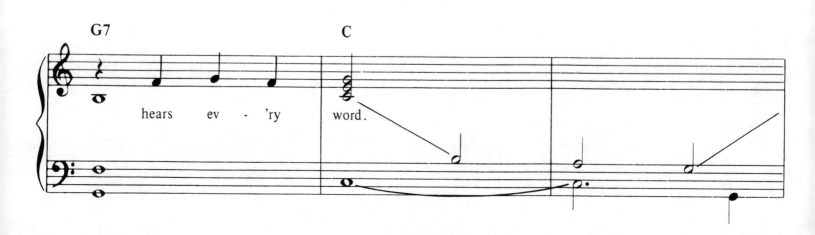

hears ev - 'ry word.

Ev - 'ry time I hear a new - born ba - by cry

poco a poco cresc.

F

B7   or touch a   E leaf,   E7 or see the

Am7   sky,_____ then I know   Dm7 why

ff

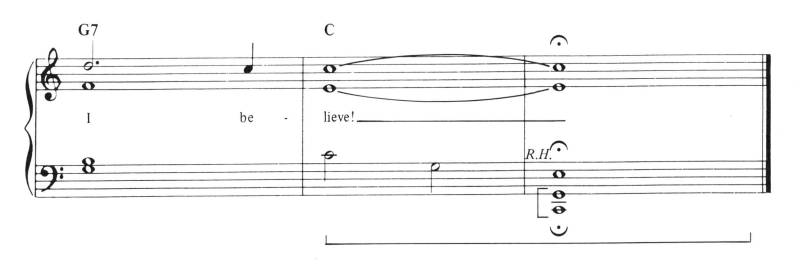

G7   I be -   C lieve!_____

R.H.

I'D LIKE TO TEACH THE WORLD TO SING
(In Perfect Harmony)

Words and Music by B. BACKER, B. DAVIS,
R. COOK and R. GREENAWAY

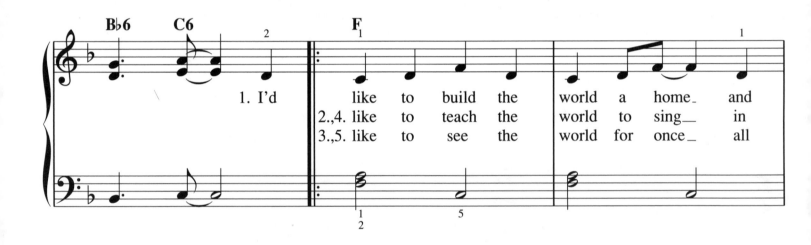

1. I'd like to build the world a home_ and
2.,4. like to teach the world to sing_ in
3.,5. like to see the world for once_ all

fur - nish in with love, grow ap - ple trees and
per - fect har - mo - ny, I'd like to hold it
stand - ing hand in hand, and hear them ech - o

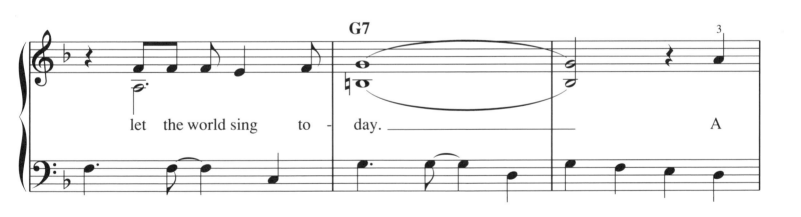

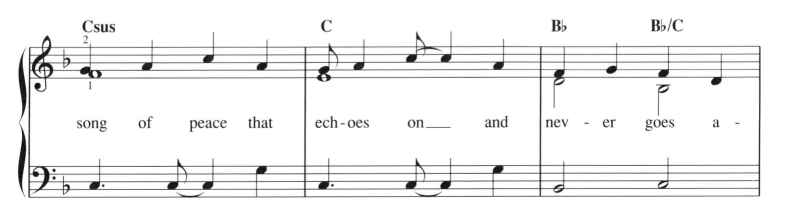

way.

F | **Csus** | **C**

Put your hand in my hand,

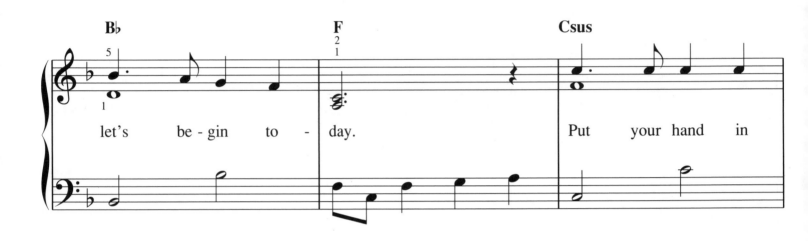

B♭ | **F** | **Csus**

let's be - gin to - day. Put your hand in

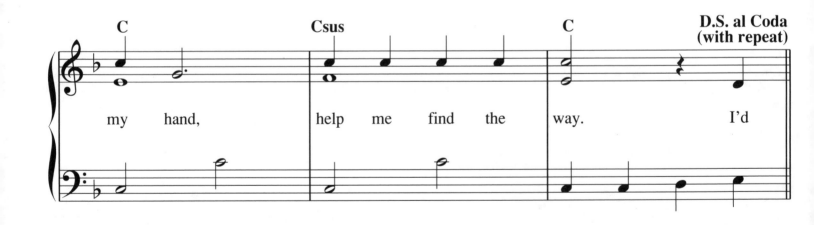

C | **Csus** | **C** | **D.S. al Coda (with repeat)**

my hand, help me find the way. I'd

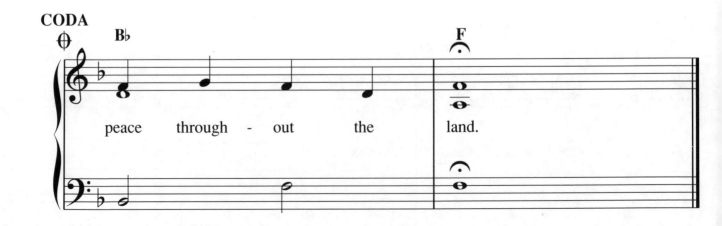

CODA | **B♭** | **F**

peace through - out the land.

IF I HAD A HAMMER
(The Hammer Song)

Words and Music by LEE HAYS
and PETE SEEGER

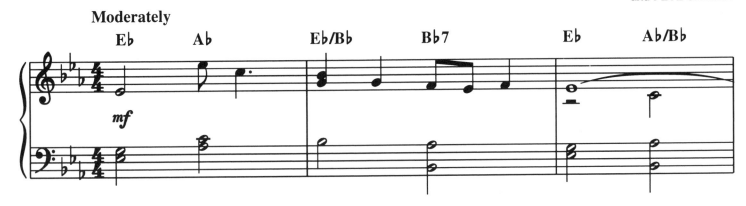

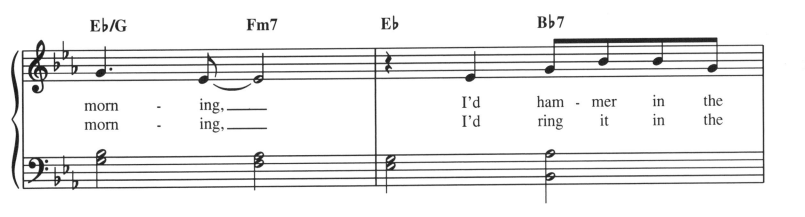

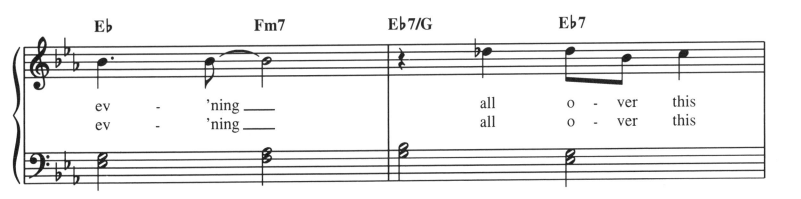

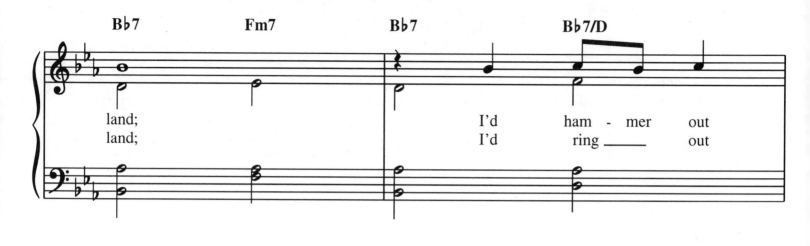

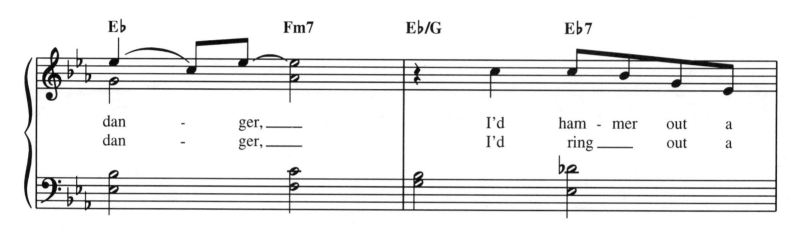

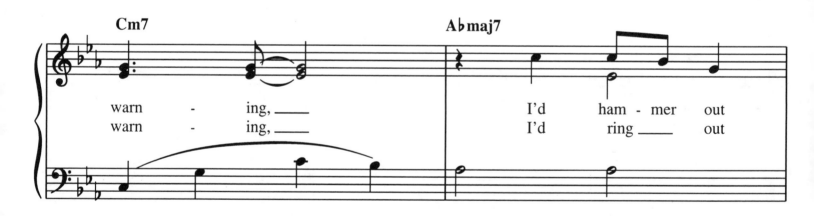

71

IMAGINE

Words and Music by
JOHN LENNON

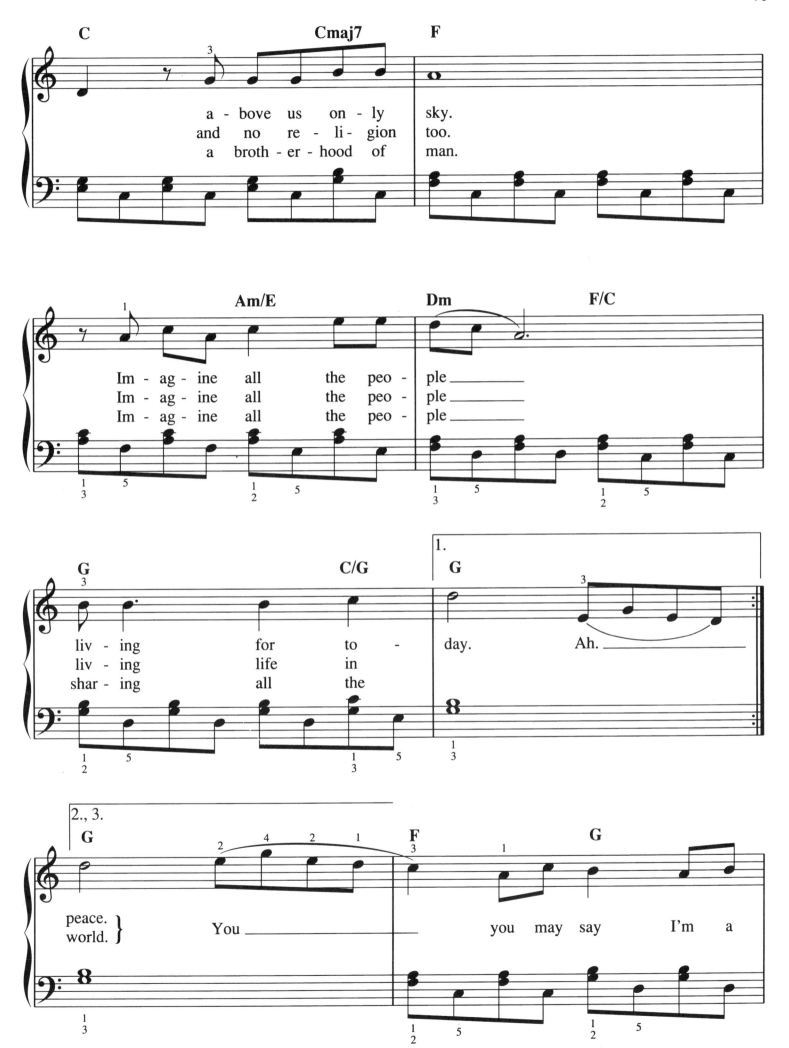

WHAT THE WORLD NEEDS NOW IS LOVE

Lyric by HAL DAVID
Music by BURT BACHARACH

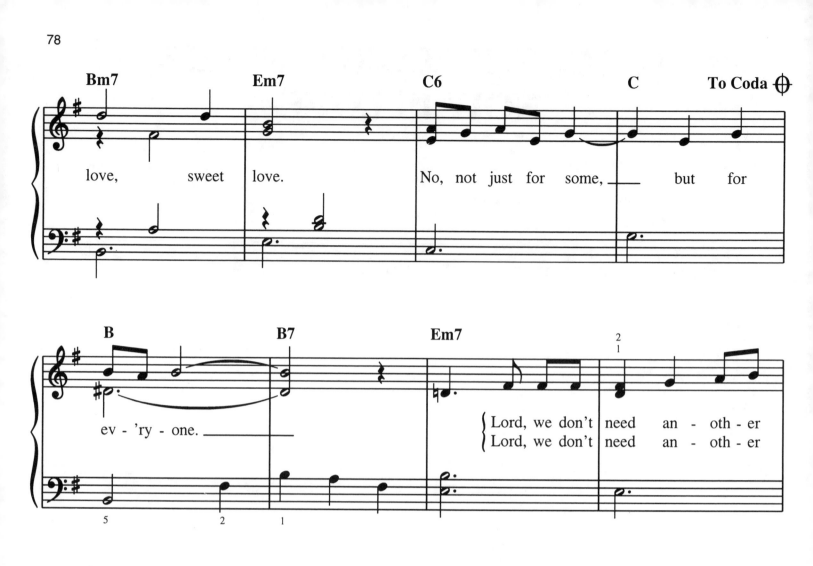

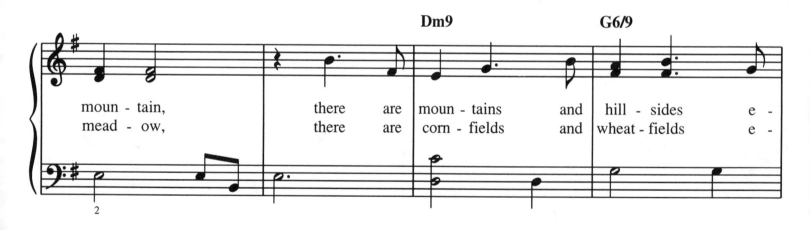

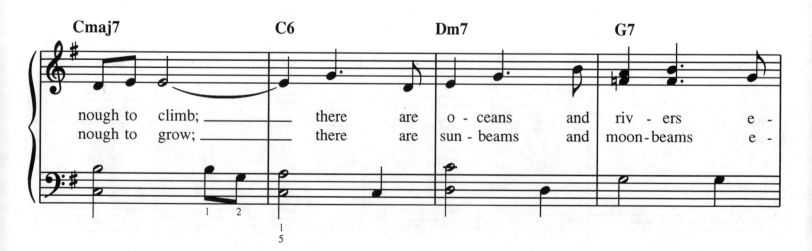

THE IMPOSSIBLE DREAM
(The Quest)
from MAN OF LA MANCHA

Lyric by JOE DARION
Music by MITCH LEIGH

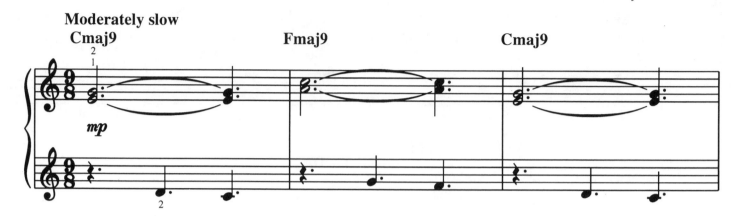

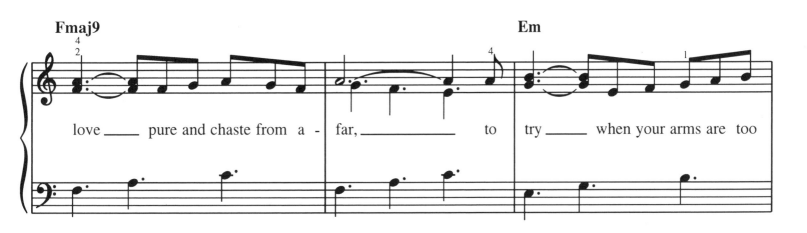

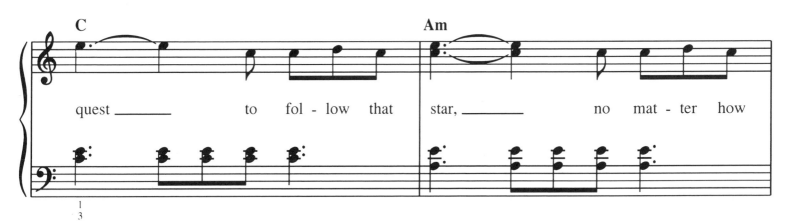

hope-less, ____ no mat-ter how far; _____ to fight for the right ___ with-out ques-tion or

pause, __ to be will-ing to march in - to hell for a heav-en - ly cause! _____ And I

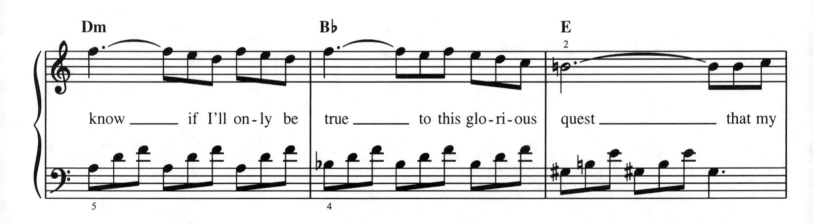

know _____ if I'll on-ly be true _____ to this glo-ri-ous quest _____ that my

heart _____ will lie peace-ful and calm _____ when I'm laid to my

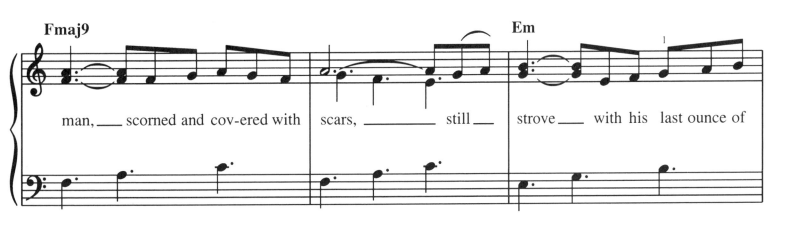

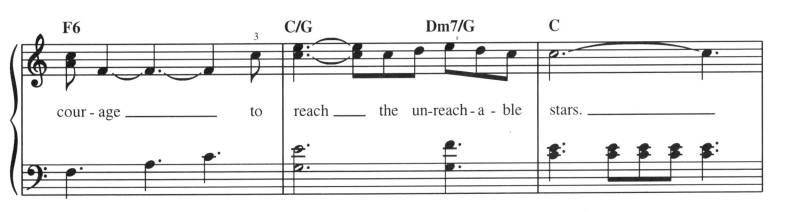

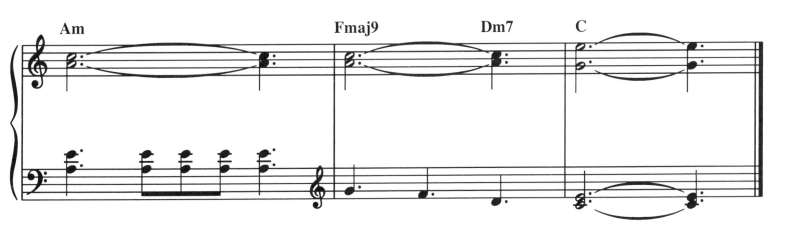

ORDINARY MIRACLES

Words by ALAN BERGMAN
and MARILYN BERGMAN
Music by MARVIN HAMLISCH

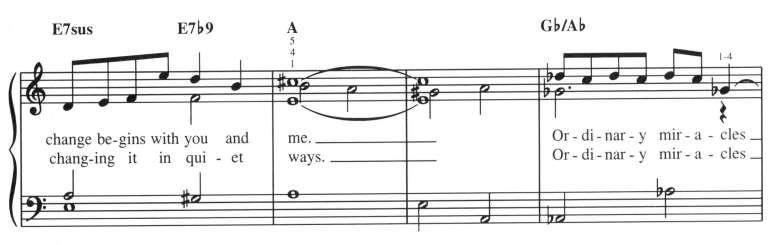

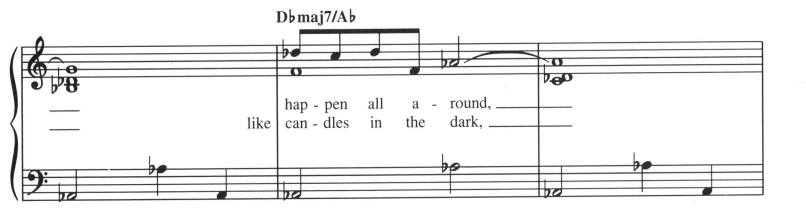

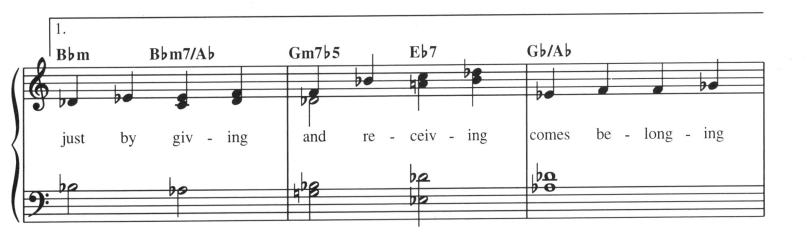

and be - liev - ing. each and ev - 'ry one of us ___ lights a

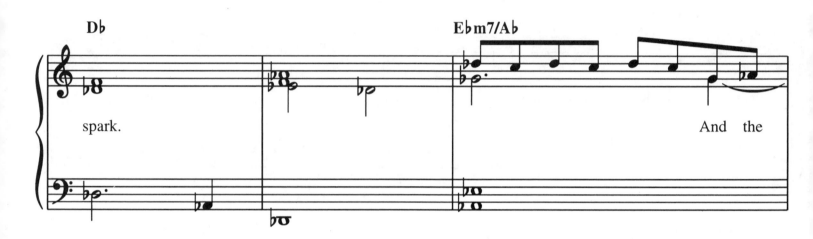

spark. And the

walls can tum - ble and the moun - tains can move.

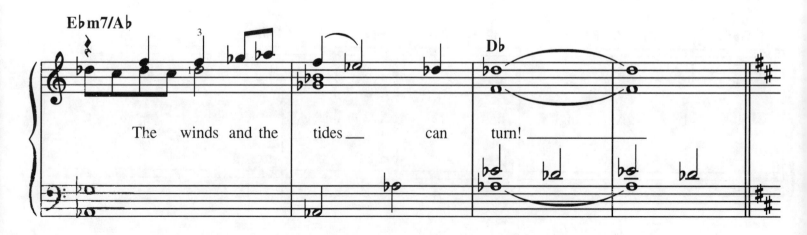

The winds and the tides ___ can turn! ___

Or - di - nar - y mir - a - cles, _____ one for ev - 'ry star. _____

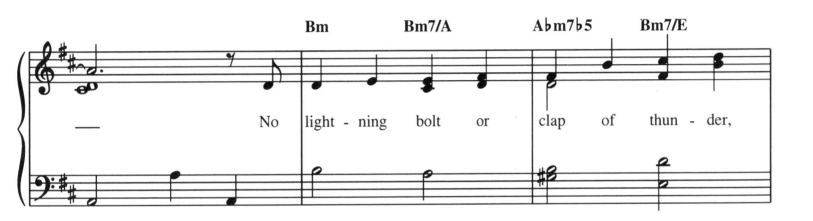

___ No light - ning bolt or clap of thun - der,

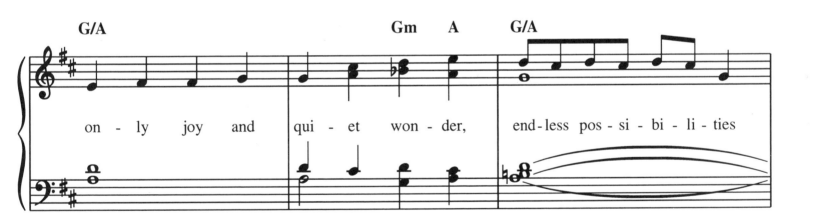

on - ly joy and qui - et won - der, end - less pos - si - bi - li - ties

right be - fore our eyes.

See the way a mir - a - cle _____ mul - ti - plies. _____

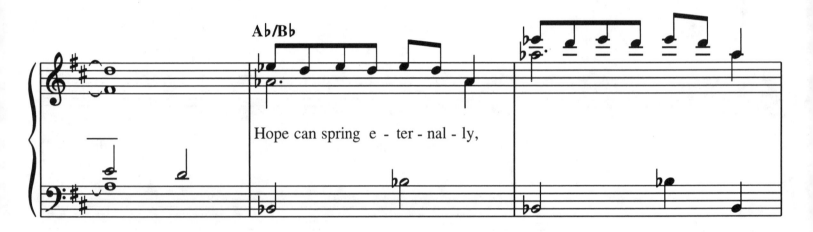

Hope can spring e - ter - nal - ly,

plant it and it grows. Love is all that's

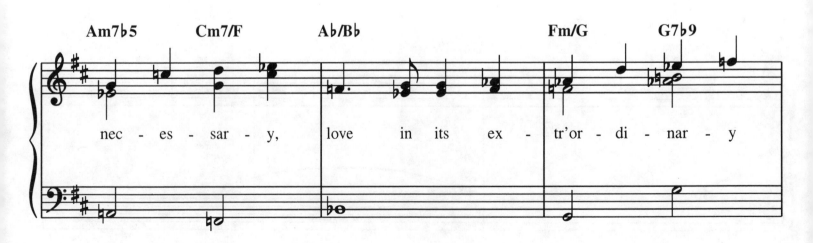

nec - es - sar - y, love in its ex - tr'or - di - nar - y

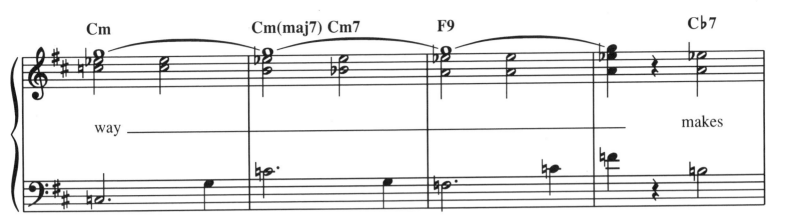

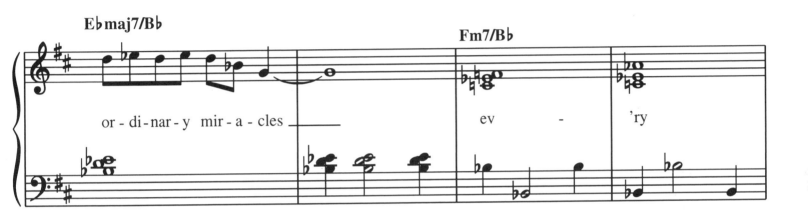

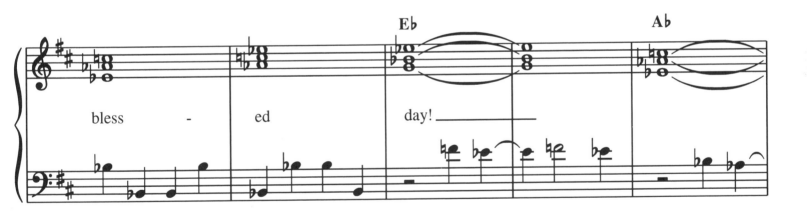

THE POWER OF THE DREAM

Words and Music by BABYFACE,
DAVID FOSTER and LINDA THOMPSON

nothing or - di - nar - y in the liv-ing of_ each day. There's a spe-cial part_ ev-'ry one of us will

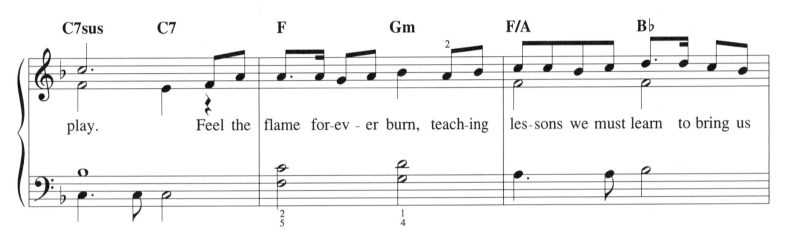

play. Feel the flame for-ev - er burn, teach-ing les-sons we must learn to bring us

clos-er to the pow - er of the dream. As the world gives us its best to stand a -

part from all_ the rest, it is the pow-er of _ the dream that brings us here.

Your

mind will take you far, the rest is just pure heart. You'll find your fate is all your own cre-

a - tion. Ev - 'ry boy and girl, as they come in - to this world, they

bring the gift of hope and in - spir - a - tion. Feel the flame for - ev - er burn, teach - ing

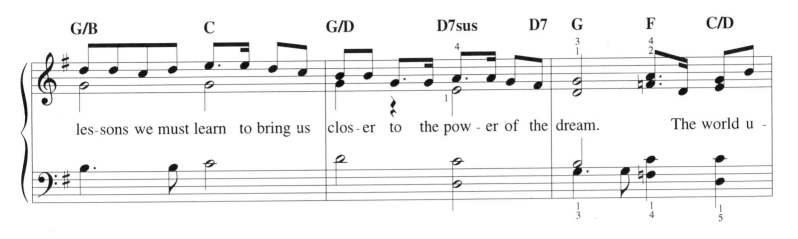

les-sons we must learn to bring us clos-er to   the pow - er of the dream.   The world u -

nites in hope and peace, pray that | it will al - ways be. It is the | pow-er of_ the dream that brings us

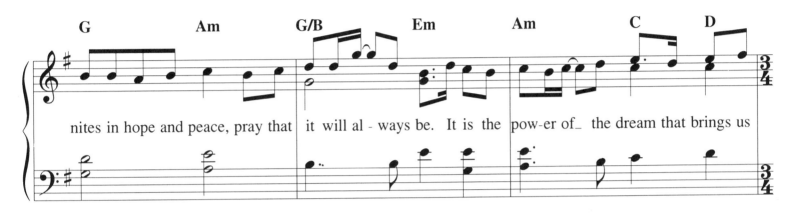

here.

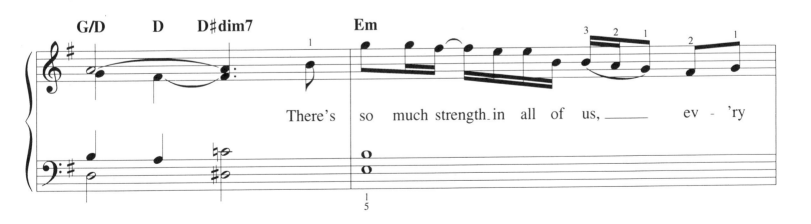

There's   so   much strength in all of us, _____   ev - 'ry

SOMEDAY
from Walt Disney's THE HUNCHBACK OF NOTRE DAME

Music by ALAN MENKEN
Lyrics by STEPHEN SCHWARTZ

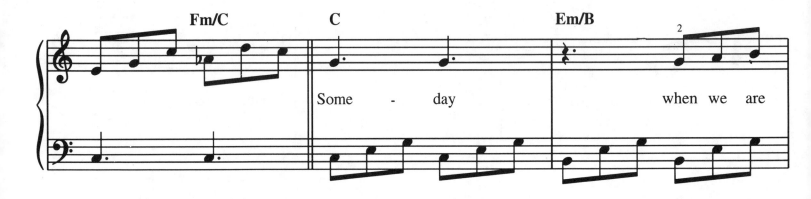

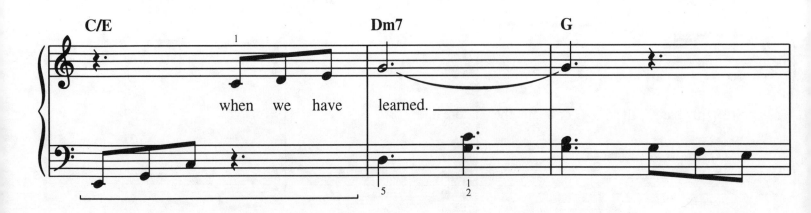

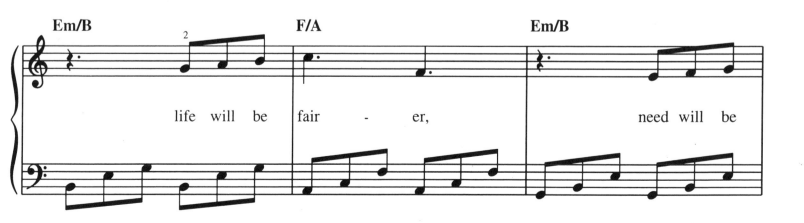

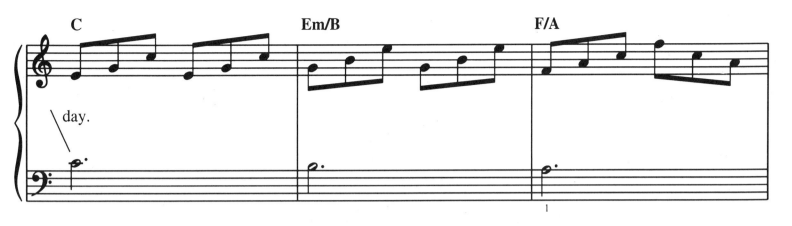

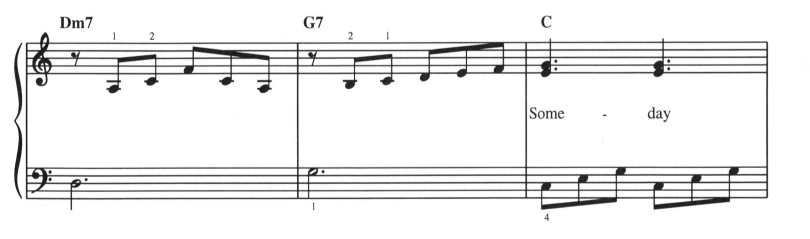

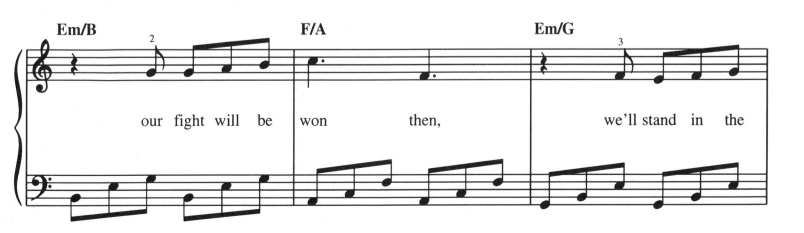

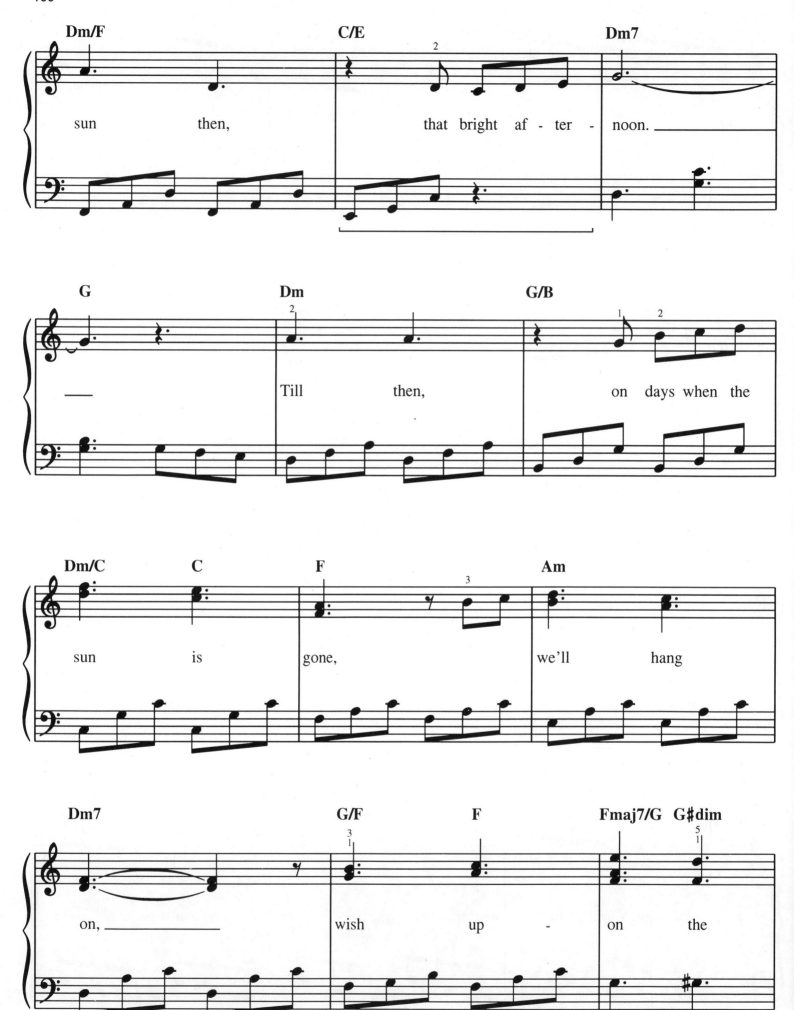

TURN! TURN! TURN!
(To Everything There Is a Season)

Words from the Book of Ecclesiastes
Adaptation and Music by PETE SEEGER

Moderately slow, in 2

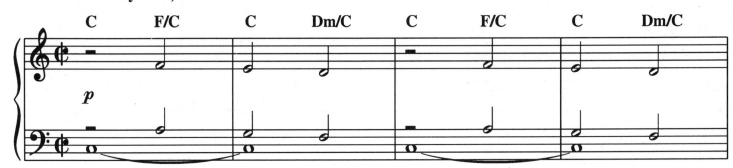

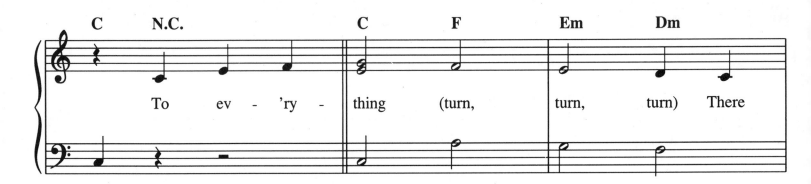

To ev-'ry-thing (turn, turn, turn) There

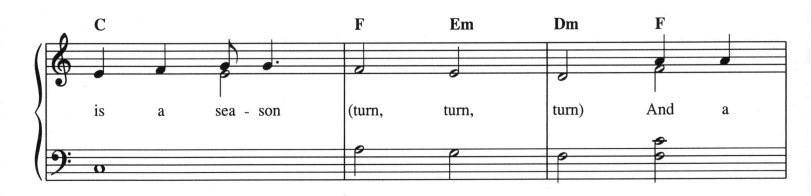

is a sea-son (turn, turn, turn) And a

time for ev-'ry pur-pose un-der heav-en.

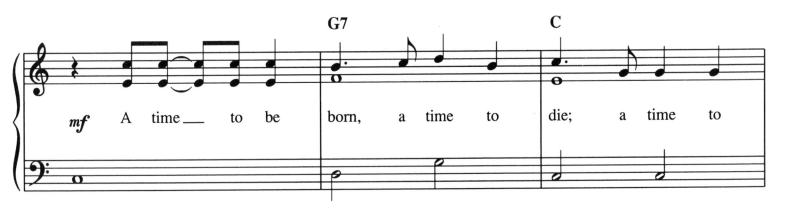

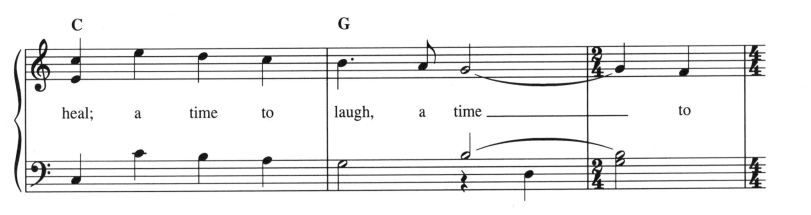

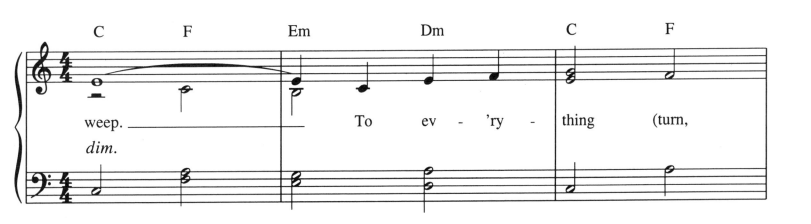

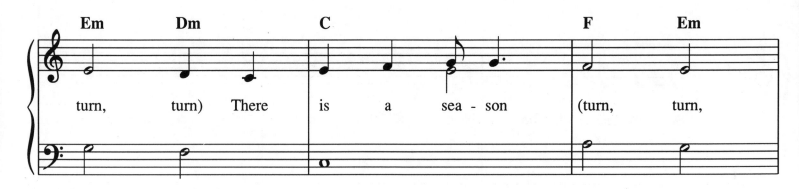

turn, turn) There is a sea - son (turn, turn,

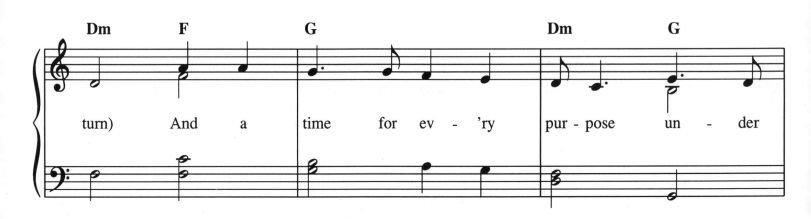

turn) And a time for ev - 'ry pur - pose un - der

heav - en. A time to build up, a time to break

down; a time to dance, a time to mourn; a

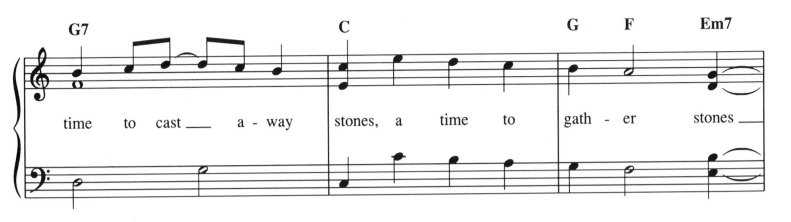

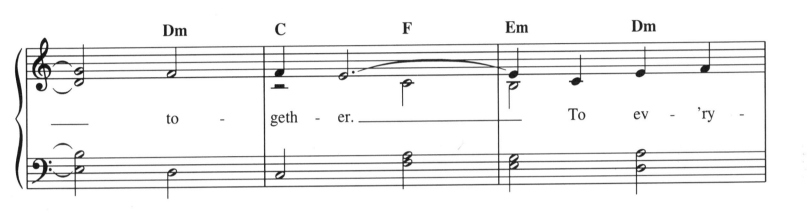

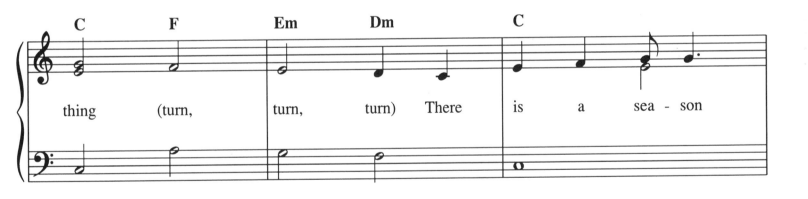

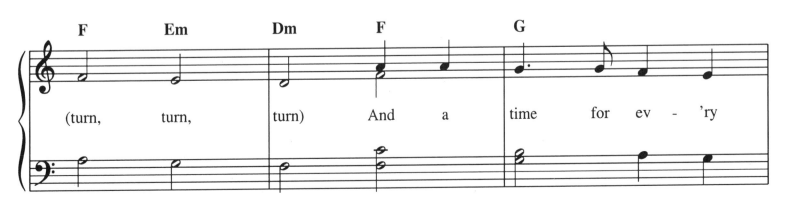

pur - pose un - der heav - en.

A time of
A time to

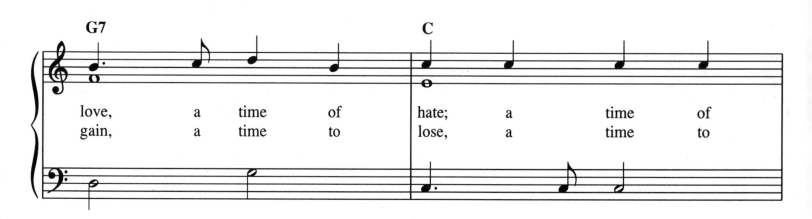

love,   a time of   hate;   a   time   of
gain,   a time to   lose,   a   time   to

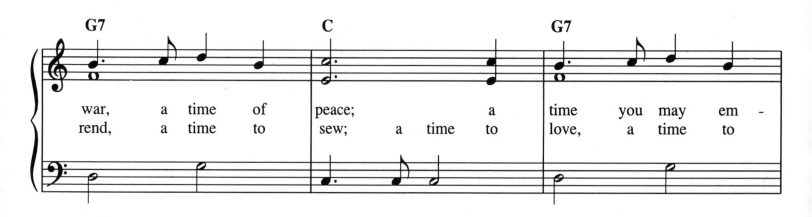

war,   a time of   peace;   a   time you may em -
rend,   a time to   sew;   a time to   love,   a time to

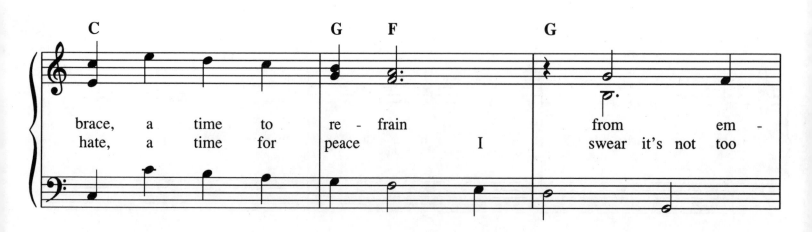

brace,   a time to   re - frain   from em -
hate,   a time for   peace   I   swear it's not too

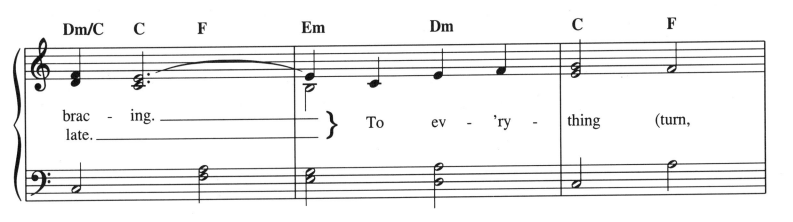

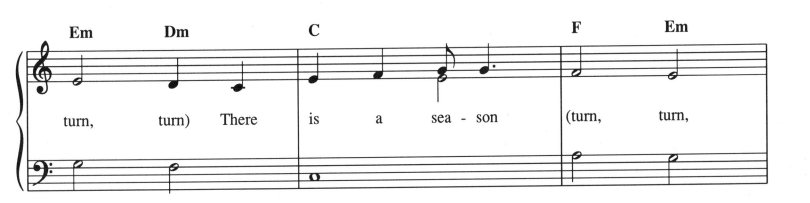

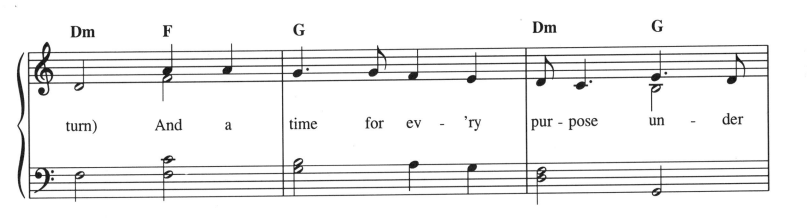

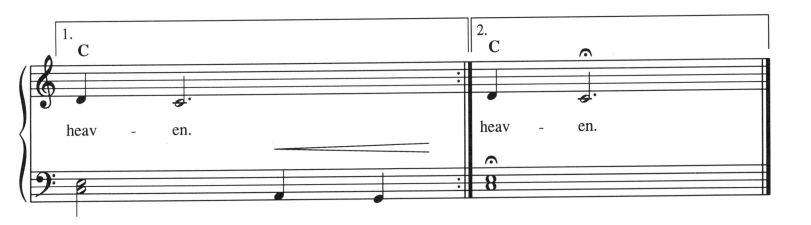

WHERE HAVE ALL THE FLOWERS GONE?

Words and Music by
PETE SEEGER

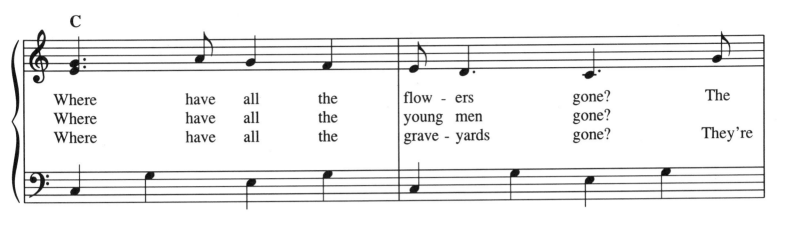

Where   have   all   the   flow - ers   gone?   The

Where   have   all   the   young men   gone?   The

Where   have   all   the   grave - yards gone?   They're

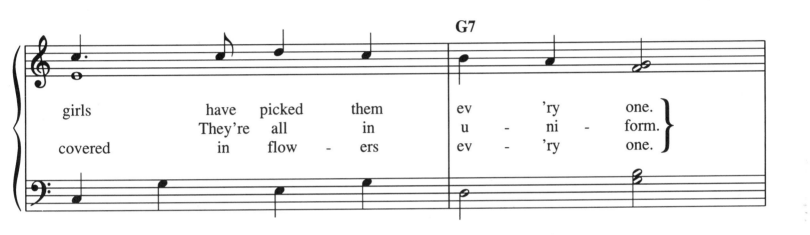

girls   have picked them   ev - 'ry   one.

            They're all   in   u - ni - form.

covered   in flow - ers   ev - 'ry   one.

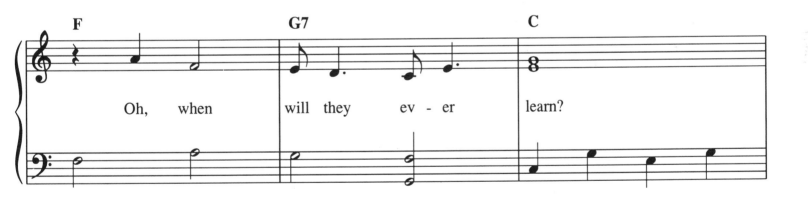

Oh,   when   will they ev - er   learn?

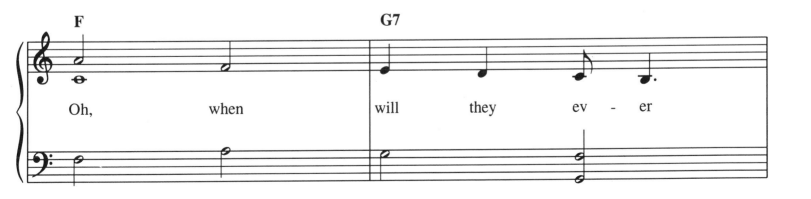

Oh,   when   will   they   ev - er

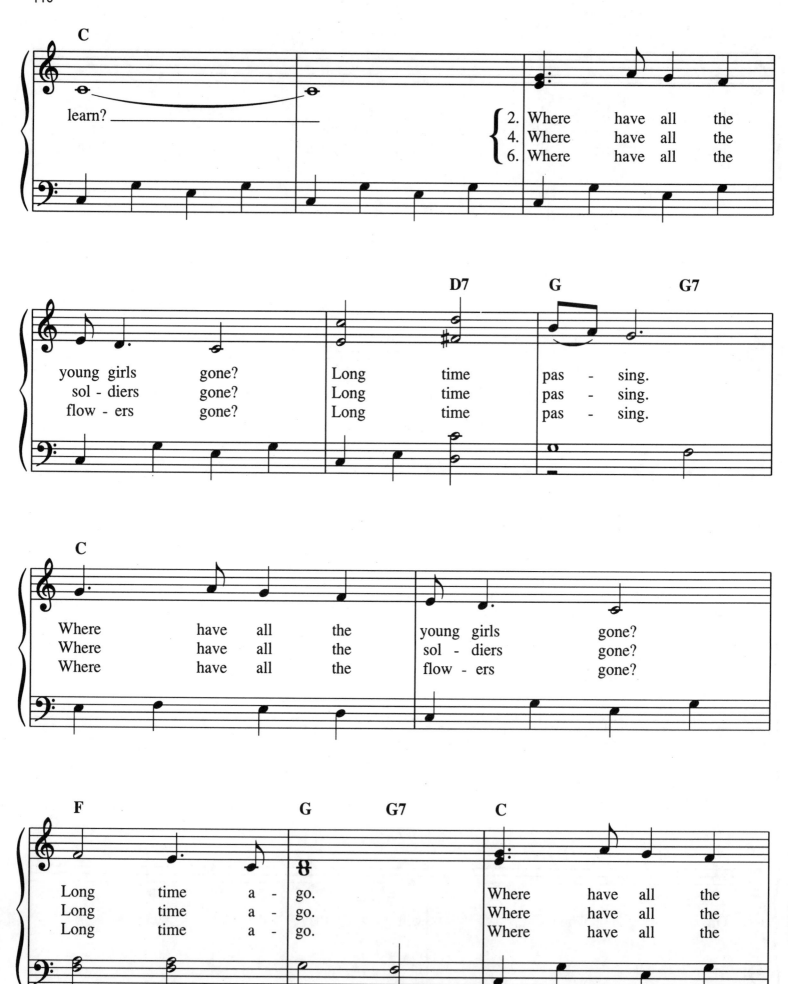

young girls   gone?   They've tak - en hus - bands
sol - diers   gone?   They've gone   to grave - yards
flow - ers   gone?   Young girls   picked them

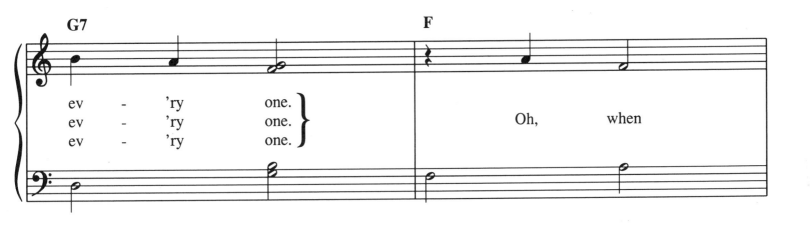

G7   **F**

ev - 'ry   one.
ev - 'ry   one.
ev - 'ry   one.   Oh,   when

G7   **C**   **F**

will they ev - er learn?   Oh,   when

G7   **C**   1.,2.   3.

will they ev - er *rit.* learn?

WITH A LITTLE HELP FROM MY FRIENDS

Words and Music by JOHN LENNON
and PAUL McCARTNEY

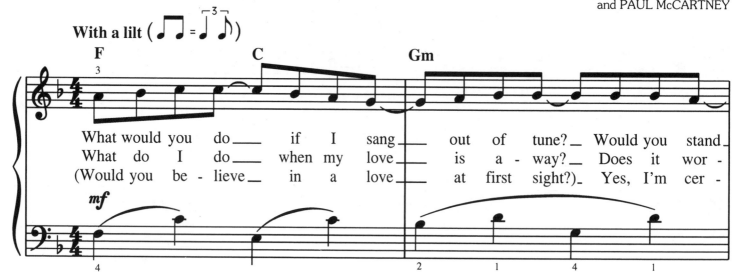

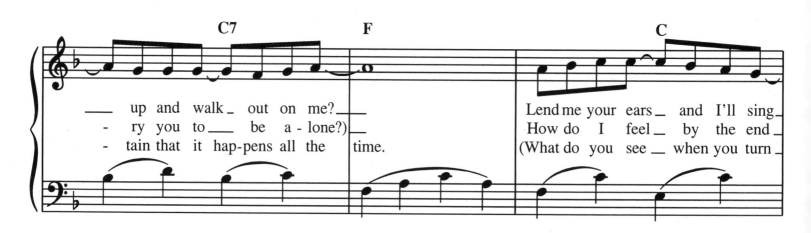

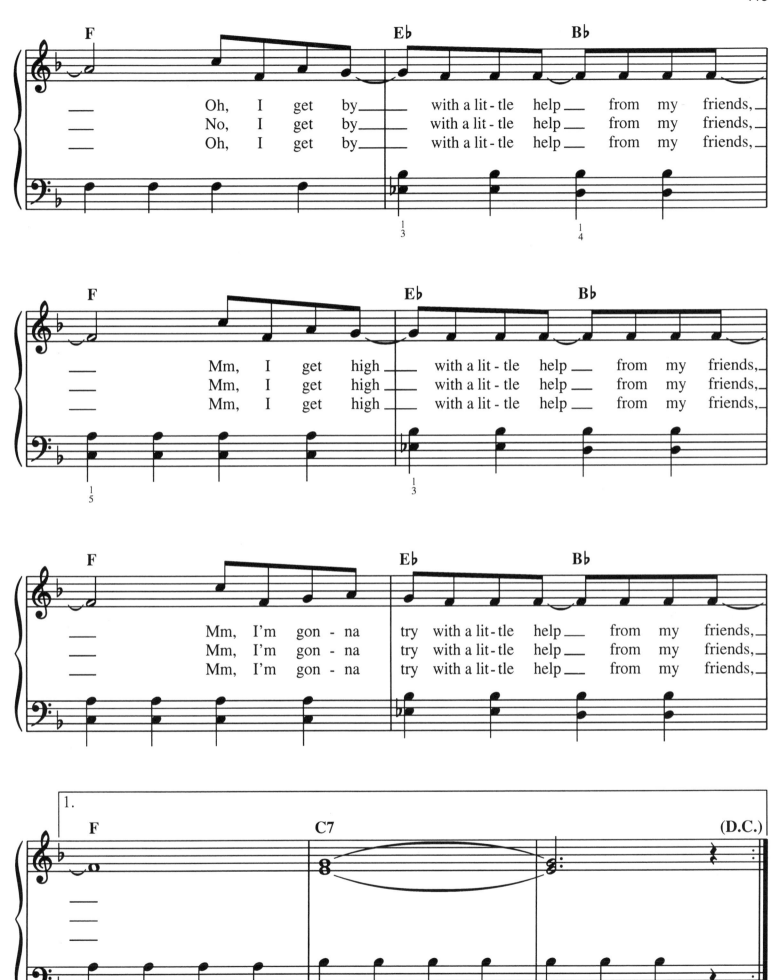

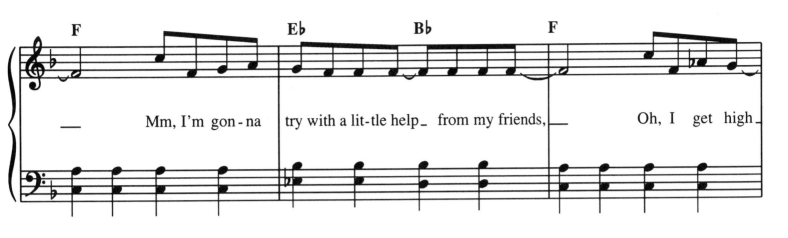

Mm, I'm gon-na try with a lit-tle help _ from my friends, _ Oh, I get high

_ with a lit-tle help _ from my friends, _ Yes, I get by _

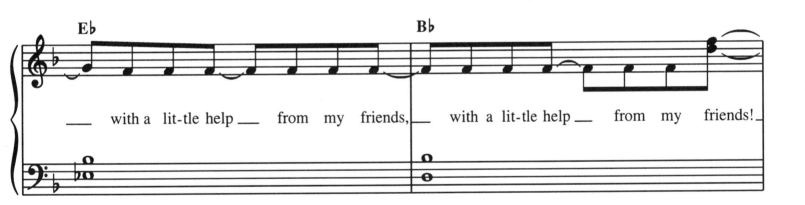

_ with a lit-tle help _ from my friends, _ with a lit-tle help _ from my friends!

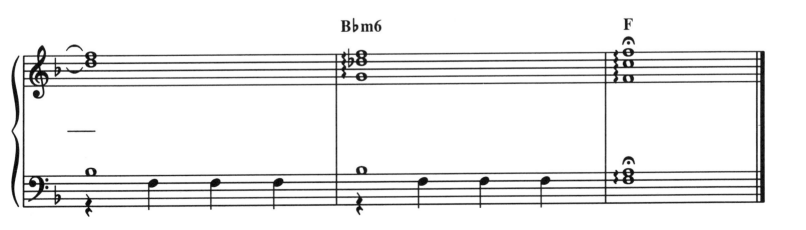

A WONDERFUL DAY LIKE TODAY

from THE ROAR OF THE GREASEPAINT-THE SMELL OF THE CROWD

Words and Music by LESLIE BRICUSSE
and ANTHONY NEWLEY

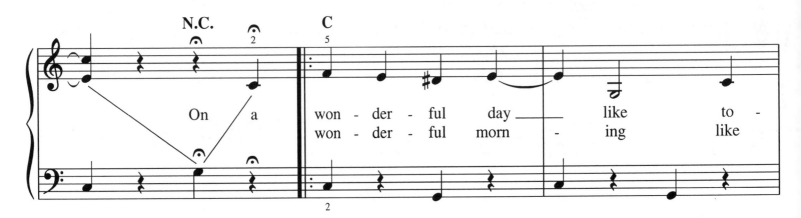

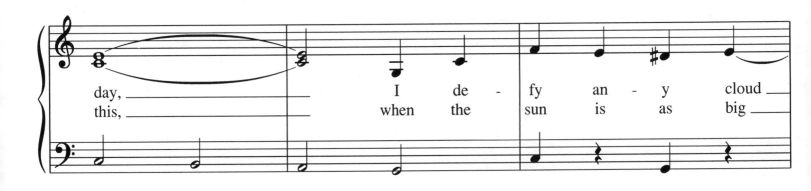

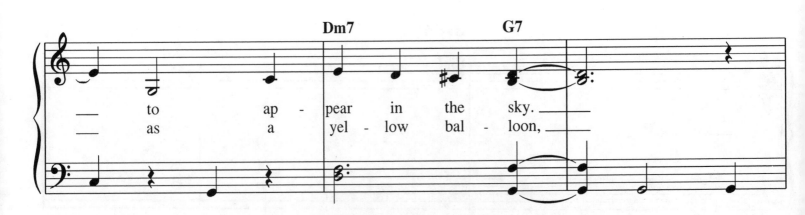

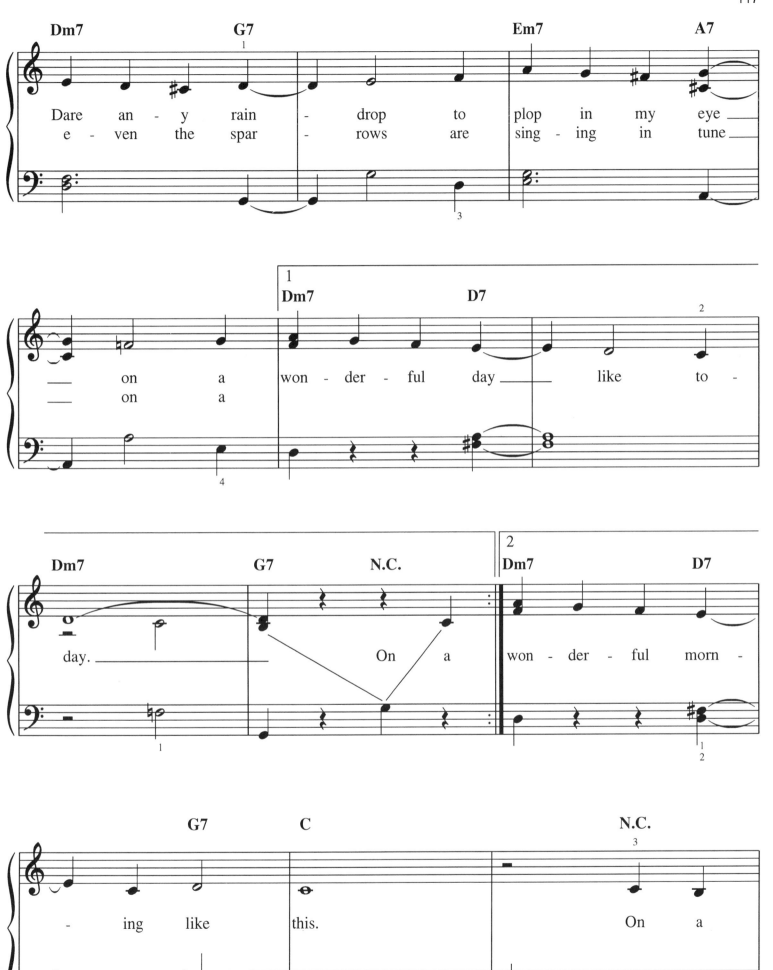

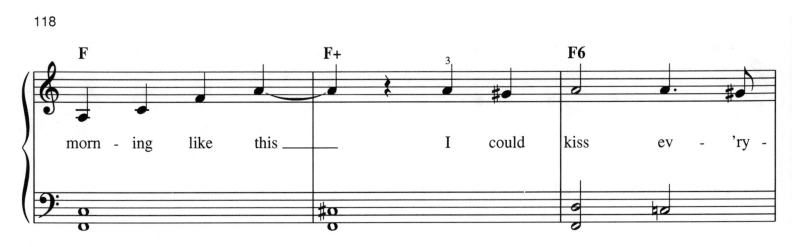

morn - ing   like   this _____   I   could   kiss   ev - 'ry -

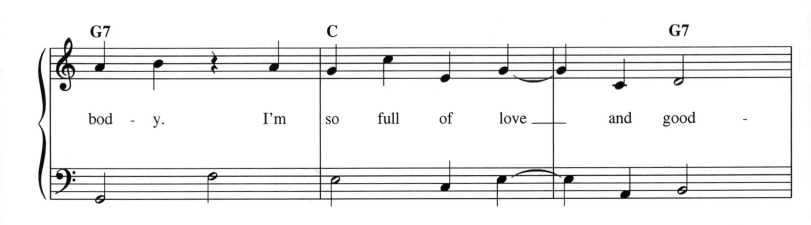

bod - y.   I'm   so   full   of   love _____   and   good -

will. _____   Let   me   say   fur - ther - more _____

_____   I'd   a - dore   ev - 'ry - bod - y   to

come and dine. The pleas - ure's mine, and I will pay the

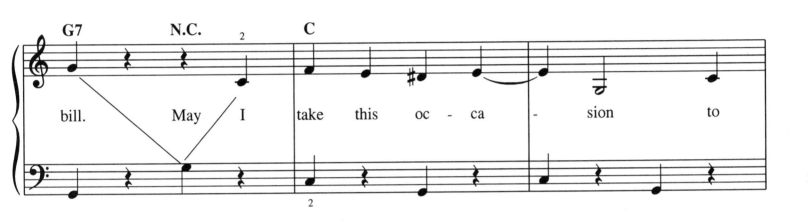

bill. May I take this oc - ca - sion to

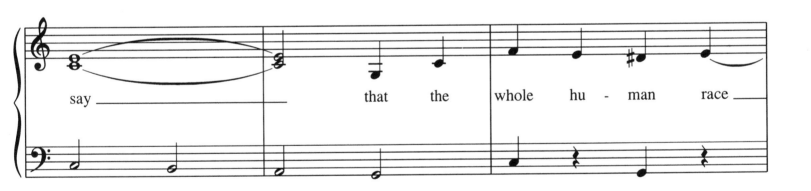

say that the whole hu - man race

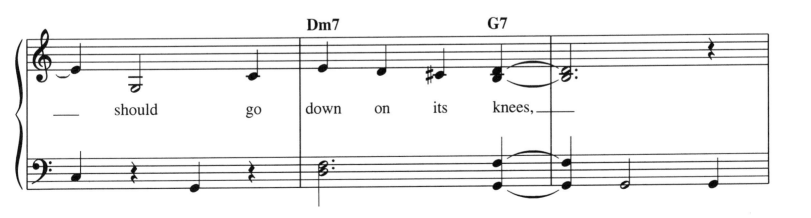

should go down on its knees,

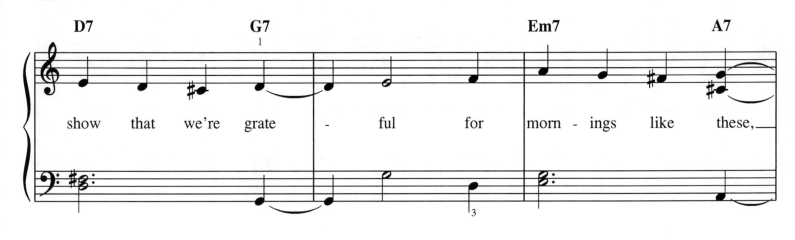

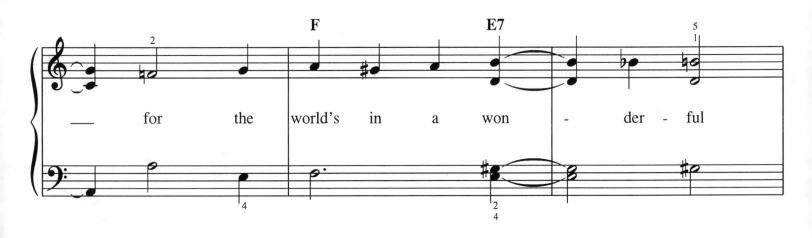

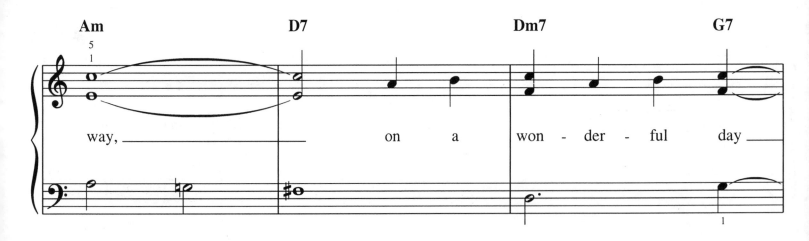

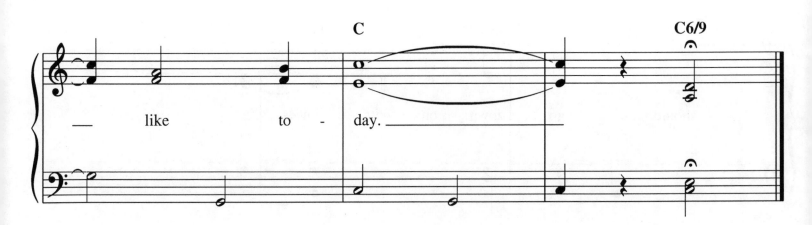

YOU'LL NEVER WALK ALONE

from CAROUSEL

Lyrics by OSCAR HAMMERSTEIN II
Music by RICHARD RODGERS

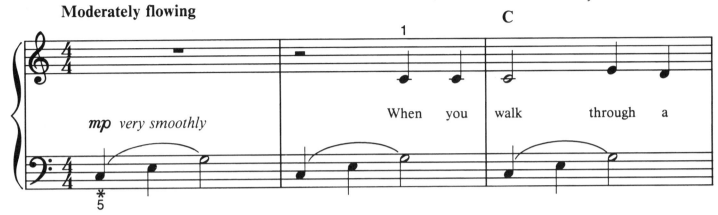

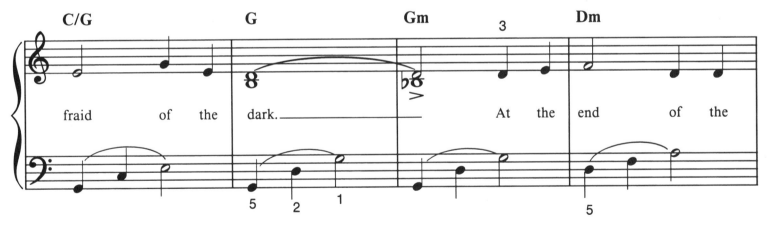

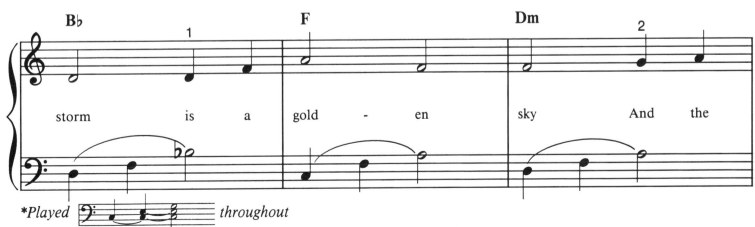

*Played throughout

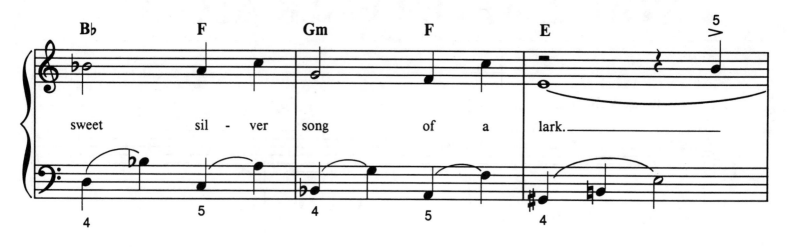

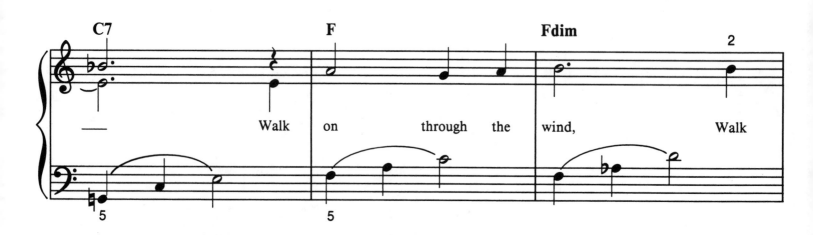

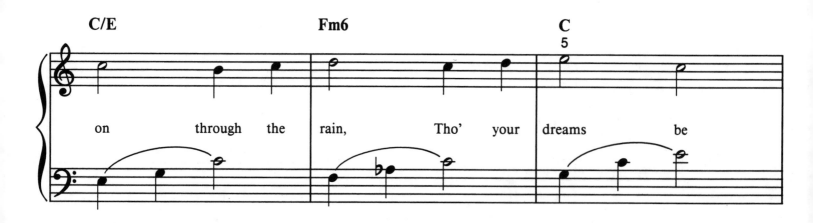

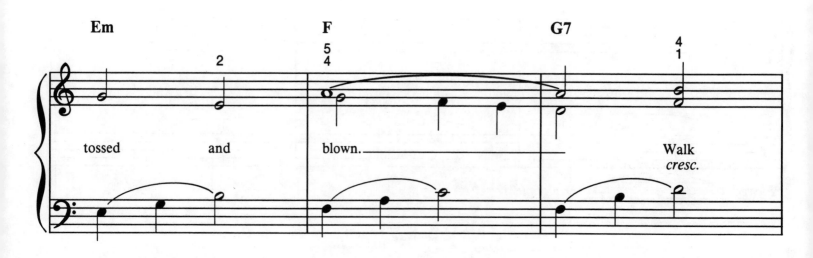

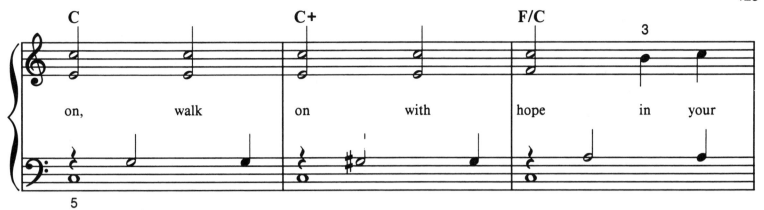

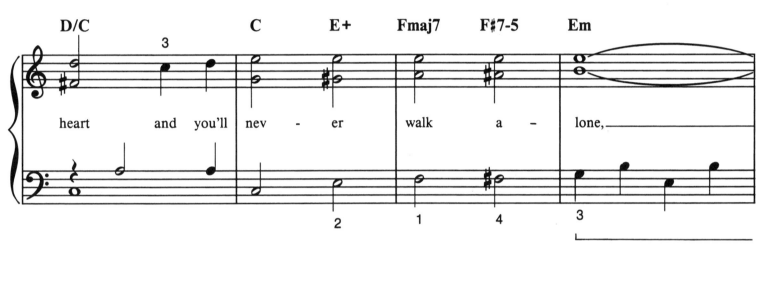

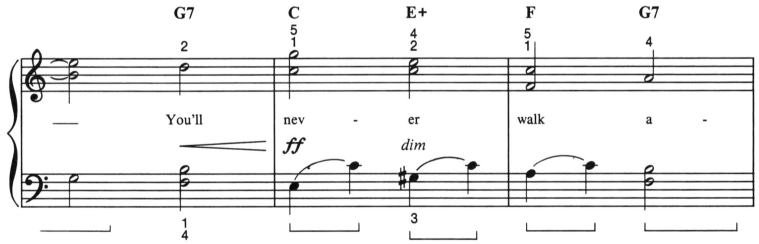

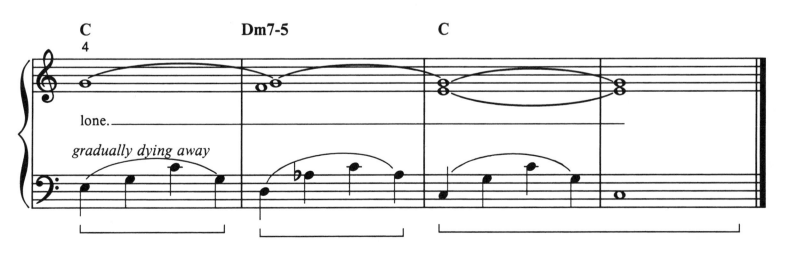

YOU'VE GOT TO BE CAREFULLY TAUGHT

from SOUTH PACIFIC

Lyrics by OSCAR HAMMERSTEIN II
Music by RICHARD RODGERS

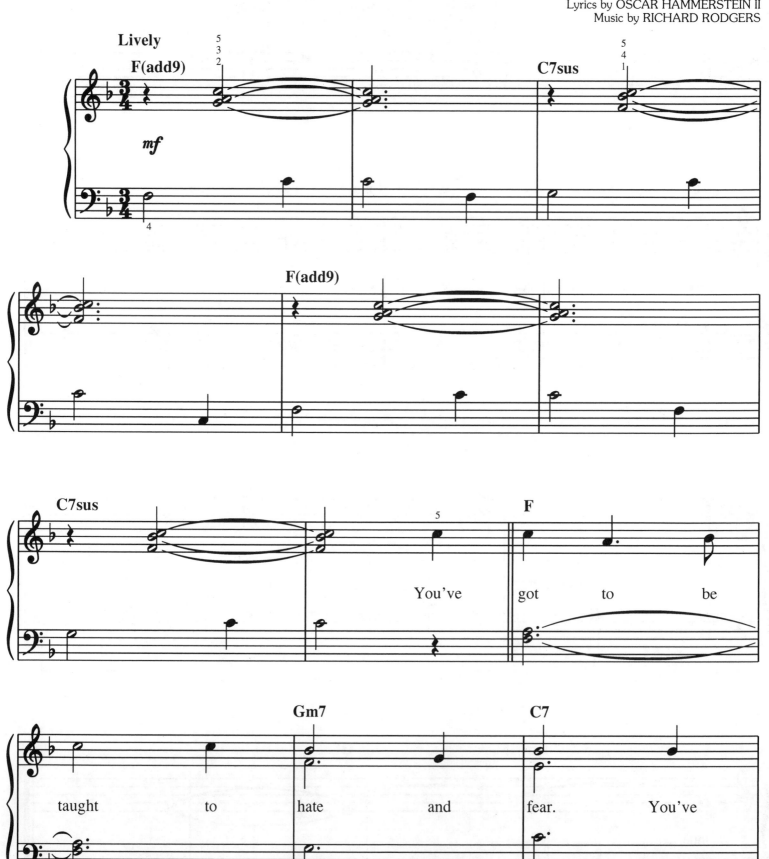

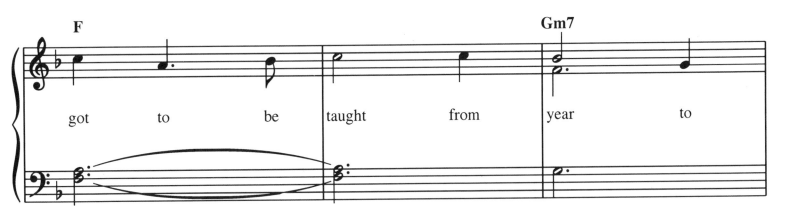

got to be | taught from | year to

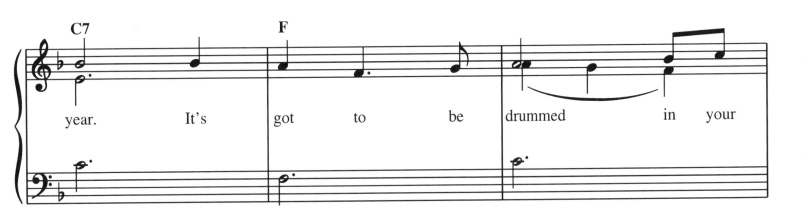

year. It's | got to be | drummed in your

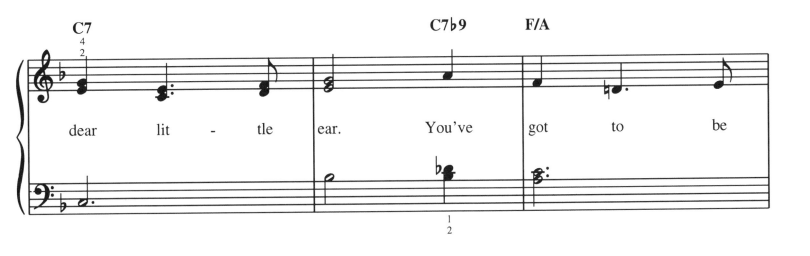

dear lit - tle ear. | You've | got to be

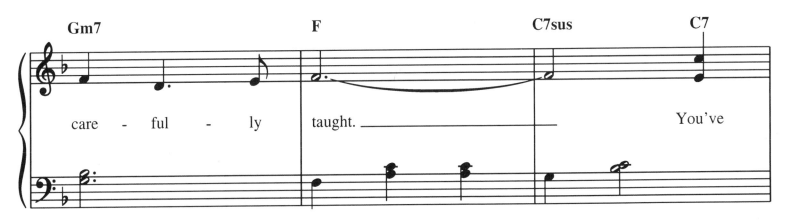

care - ful - ly | taught. _____ | | You've

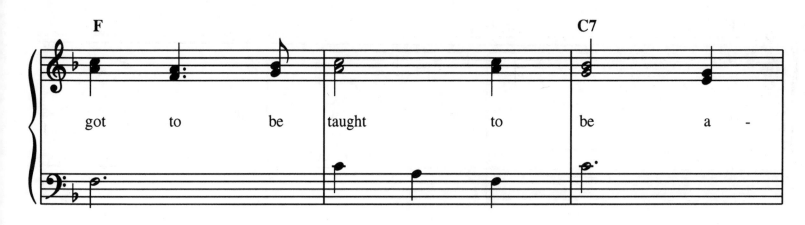

got to be taught to be a -

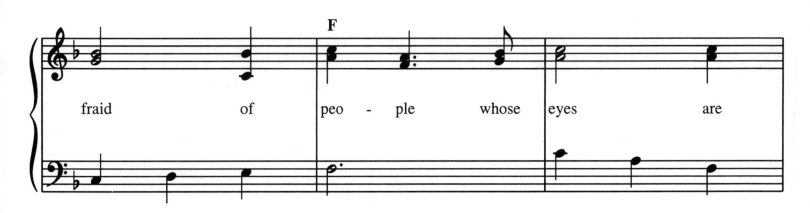

fraid of peo - ple whose eyes are

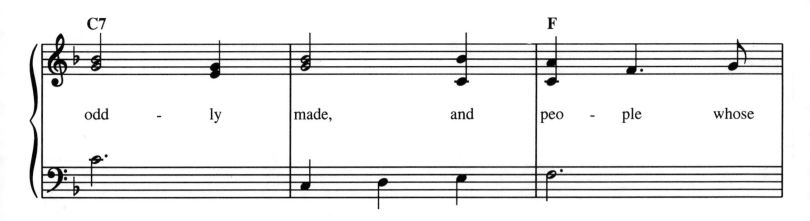

odd - ly made, and peo - ple whose

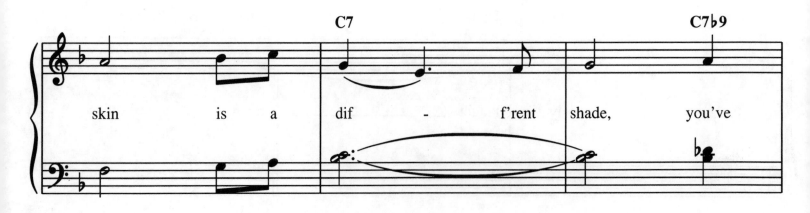

skin is a dif - f'rent shade, you've

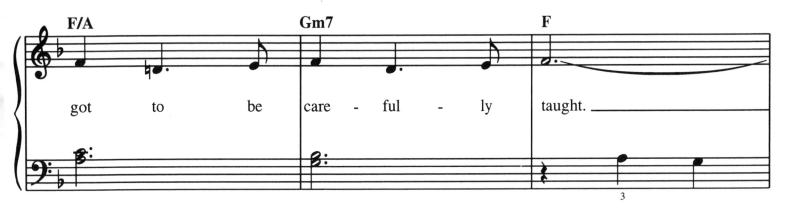

got to be care - ful - ly taught. _____

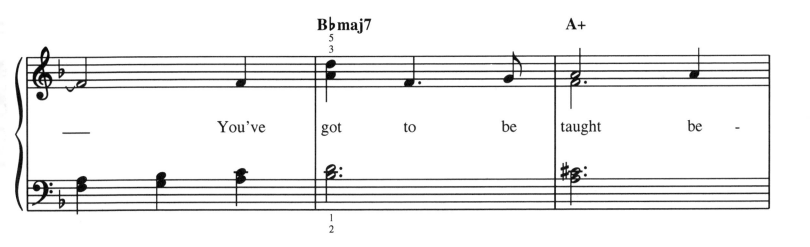

_____ You've got to be taught be -

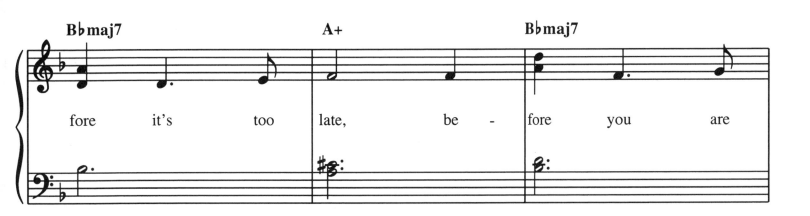

fore it's too late, be - fore you are

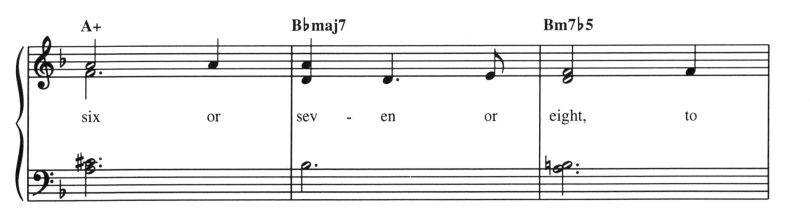

six or sev - en or eight, to

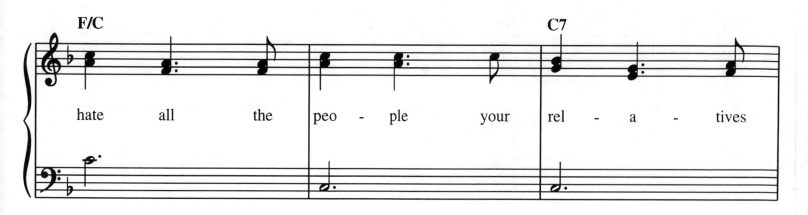

hate all the peo - ple your rel - a - tives

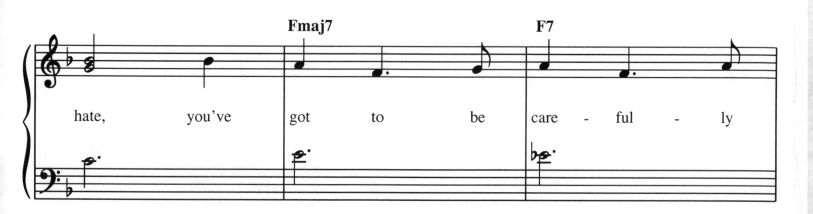

hate, you've got to be care - ful - ly

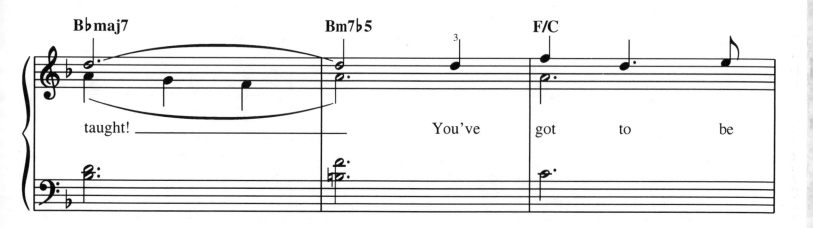

taught! _____ You've got to be

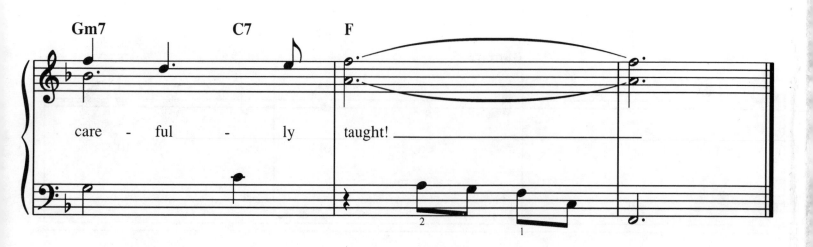

care - ful - ly taught! _____